FLOODS ACROSS EUROPE

Hazard assessment, modelling and management

*Edited by Edmund C. Penning-Rowsell
and Maureen Fordham*

Middlesex University Press

© Flood Hazard Research Centre

First published in 1994 by Middlesex University Press.
Middlesex University Press is an imprint of Middlesex University Services Limited,
Bounds Green Road, London N11 2NQ.

First reprint 1985

A CIP Catalogue record for this book is available
from the British Library.

ISBN 1 898253 01 3

© Cover image made by DRA supplied by
Earth Images Picture Library, Bristol

Editorial, design and production in association with
Book Production Consultants plc, 25–27 High Street,
Chesterton, Cambridge CB4 1ND
Typeset by Cambridge Photosetting Services
and printed by
Ipswich Book Co. Ltd., Ipswich, Suffolk.

List of Contents

Preface

This volume contains a summary of our EUROflood research project, the first phase of which began in March 1992 and finished in February 1994. It therefore comprises part of our final report on this stage of our work for the European Commission, which has sponsored the research.

The objective of the EUROflood I research project was to improve our understanding of the causes, impacts and responses to flood hazards in the countries of the European Union. The project team has comprised economists, geographers, civil engineers, regional scientists, sociologists, planners and ecologists.

The research in the EUROflood project has been organised in a number of modules, each of which involves two or more partners:

- Climate scenarios and model integration (Delft Hydraulics and Middlesex University). The best scientific analysis of future climate scenarios has been synthesised in this module, and the various models being developed in the project are being integrated into a coherent flood impact appraisal system. This module has contributed to Chapters 2, 4 and 5 in this volume.
- Full flood impacts (Middlesex University, the University of Twente, CERGRENE and LNEC). The impacts of floods on vulnerable populations has been analysed, with emphasis on the 'intangible' impacts and sediment load resulting in damage. This module has contributed to Chapters 3 and 7 in this volume.
- Regional-scale modelling (Braschel and Schmitz and Delft Hydraulics). Many techniques have been developed for small-scale flood impact analysis; this module has explored the development of methods and models for regional-scale strategic analysis for policy/priority setting. This material has contributed to Chapters 4 and 5 in this volume.

- Flood warning effectiveness (Middlesex University and CERGRENE). Flood warning systems are only as good as the dissemination systems that they feed. This module has analysed those systems and their effectiveness, and contributes material to Chapters 3 and 6 of this volume.
- Safety standards (Delft Hydraulics and the University of Twente). This module has analysed the safety of current flood alleviation measures, developed methods to analyse this safety, and developed techniques for determining priorities for raising standards where appropriate. This research has contributed to Chapter 5 in this volume.
- Interface with the public (IST, LNEC and Middlesex University). The public often does not understand flood problems and flood alleviation measures; this module has been testing different methods of interfacing policy development with the public, so that the public acceptability of flood alleviation measures is improved.

The partners in this research and their organisations are listed below. In the second phase of the research we are adding partners in Spain (LIM; University of Barcelona) and Italy (Instituto di Idraulica, Catania):

Edmund Penning-Rowsell, Maureen Fordham, Colin Green and Dennis Parker
   Flood Hazard Research Centre (Research Coordinator)
   Middlesex University
   Queensway
   Enfield
   Middlesex, EN3 4SF
   United Kingdom

Bart Peerbolte
   Delft Hydraulics
   PO Box 152
   8300 AD Emmeloord
   The Netherlands

Anne van der Veen, Erik Wierstra and Herman Wind
  University of Twente, Departments of Public Policy (BSK) and Civil
  Engineering and Management
  PO Box 217, 7500 AE
  The Netherlands

Walter Pflügner, Reinhard F. Schmidtke and Joachim Klaus
  Braschel and Schmitz
  Gernerstrasse 19
  D-8000 München
  Germany

Francisco Nunes Correia and Maria da Graça Saraiva
  Departamento de Engenharia Civil
  Instituto Superior Tecnico
  Av. Rovisco Pais
  1096 Lisboa
  Portugal

Jean Philippe Torterotot
  ENPC-CERGRENE
  La Courtine
  F-93167 Noisy-le-Grand, CEDEX
  France

João Rocha
  Hydrology and River Hydraulics Division
  Laboratorio Nacional de Engenharia Civil (LNEC)
  Av. Brasil 1010
  P-1799 Lisboa Codex
  Portugal

The EUROflood project is sponsored by the Commission of the European Union under its EPOCH programme (European Programme on Climatology and Natural Hazards). EPOCH's aims are to provide scientific and technical support for the Union's environmental policy. It is sub-divided into four research areas: past climates and climate change, climate processes and models, climate impacts and climate-related hazards, and seismic hazards.

Within the third of these the EUROflood project is undertaking basic research on the causes, impacts and response to flooding, and also developing policy instruments for general application.

All the partners listed above have collaborated fully in the research and in our interchanges at workshops in England, the Netherlands, Germany, Portugal and France. As a result of this truly multi-disciplinary and international project we hope that our research will assist in policy development, and be used by local authorities, regional agencies and government departments working in this field.

Our project is continuing into a second stage – EUROflood II – and through this we are embarked on two more years' work. This, coupled with the current volume and its technical annexes giving more detailed research results will, we hope, develop data and methods for Europe-wide application, so as to help the different European countries to harmonise their policies, work to common standards and reduce the vulnerability of their populations to the flood hazards that they face.

Edmund C. Penning-Rowsell
and Maureen Fordham
Middlesex University
Flood Hazard Research Centre
London
7 February 1994

Acknowledgements

The authors would like to record their thanks to the large number of people who have contributed to our research and to this publication.

At Middlesex University, we would like to thank Celine Ottman for her organisation of the EUROflood project in its early phases. Kathy Ingrey and Josie Difrancesco deserve much praise for their invaluable work on the manuscript and other EUROflood matters. Sue Tapsell also made an important contribution to assisting with the many references in the text, and Steve Chilton, Paul Joyce and Nicholas Beesley worked hard on the many illustrations.

We also would like to thank the Editorial Board of the Middlesex University Press, and particularly Professor Dennis Hardy, for their support throughout this project and their careful delineation of tight deadlines.

The research at Middlesex would not have been possible without contributions from John Chatterton, John Handmer, Alison Herring, Anne-Michelle Ketteridge and Sylvia Tunstall and from the National Rivers Authority Thames Region, which sponsored the BOCDAM research.

At Delft Hydraulics and the University of Twente we would like to thank H.J.G. Koehorst, Erik Wierstra and Els Overkamp.

In Portugal we would like to thank Ruí Gonçalves Henriques (President of CNIG), Ruí Alves and Ruí Almeida (researchers at CNIG).

In Germany we would like to thank the Federal Ministry of Food, Agriculture and Forestry, which initiated the research into regional-scale analysis; the Ministry of the Environment of Lower Saxony, Hanover, which supported the empirical case studies; and the regional and local authorities in the Wesermarsch District.

In France we would like to thank Gilles Hubert.

All the authors would like to thank the European Commission for sponsoring the research, and Dr R. Fantechi and Dr M.E. Almeida Teixeira for their support over many years.

All those named above have assisted in some way in the production of this book. However, any errors or omissions remain the responsibility of the authors.

List of Figures and Tables

TABLES

CHAPTER 1

Concepts, Policies and Research

Edmund Penning-Rowsell and Bart Peerbolte

CURRENT AND FUTURE FLOOD THREATS

Almost every winter somewhere in Europe rivers overflow their banks and flood property, communication systems and disrupt economic activities. Storms, high tides and surges along our coasts create threatening situations from the combined effects of erosion and flooding.

And almost every summer there are severe thunderstorm events somewhere in Europe that produce intense rainfall, sudden rises in river levels and flooding in urban areas, and the damage and disruption that these can cause. Loss of life in floods such as these is an annual event in Europe, and every few years this rises to a scale that attracts international attention and concern.

We see in these events the way that humans have not yet 'conquered' the forces of nature. We have spent decades and centuries managing our rivers and coastlines, at vast expense, and yet these forces of nature still act in ways that both surprise and harm us. We are not in control of our destiny in this field of endeavour, and yet the public thinks that we are. Its expectations have risen, so that flooding is considered something that should not happen in modern society: our own and – more probably – the state's efforts should be protecting us from these forces.

But of course it is very often quite simply our own actions that have created the situations in which flood threats continue, or grow. We build our towns and cities in areas liable to flooding because the flat lands of flood plains are those most suitable for industrial, commercial and residential developments. The people of Europe like to live beside benign rivers and in their attractive landscapes, close to the heritage sites that were located many years ago to afford river bridging points or give access to the river or coast for navigation and water supply. We also like to live and holiday at the coast – preferably in hotels and holiday homes built as close to the beach as possible.

We also resent paying our local and national taxes to improve our often dilapidated urban drainage systems. The feeling is that what is out of sight underground is not important and in any case is someone else's problem. Public expenditure on river and coastal works is easy prey for budget-cutting finance departments that are eager to balance their budgets on a year-by-year basis; such expenditure can be delayed without major political controversy – until the next flood comes.

And, of course, the next flood will come. The inexorable statistics of flood events show that minor storms will occur several times a year, and that the 10 year flood will occur on average once every ten years, and every now and again the 100 or 200 year flood will strike. It may not be tomorrow, next year or even the year after. But it will come.

And furthermore we have climate change (Chapter 2). Sea-level rise as a result looks like a certainty, affecting both protected coasts such as that of the Netherlands and disrupting sea outfalls of rivers and urban drainage systems. The effect inland is less clear: increased precipitation and storminess seem likely, but they will differ in different regions: southern Europe is likely to be drier and northern Europe wetter. Drier conditions would reduce vegetation growth, resulting in more rapid river run-off and greater erosion. Increased flooding could result indirectly from the changed river channel geometry: the river beds will fill with sediment, leaving greater run-off volumes spilling on to flood plains. And, of course, our inability to prevent some types of flood hazard we now experience contrasts with the possibility of influencing climate change into the future.

Some of these predictions are conjectural at this stage, but what is clear is that at least the current magnitude of European flood problems will continue and that sea-level rise will add to the problems already being experienced at our coasts. We are, of course, here dealing with differences in time scale, and these differences are hard to reconcile. Thus short-term policies tend to dominate budget allocation on the one hand, but any increase in the severity of flood hazards will occur over the long term, gradually and unavoidably by the intensification of land use in the catchment areas of rivers and coastal flood plains. Climate change is also over a long term and the danger is that short-term expediency will suppress long-term thinking and strategic planning.

OUR FUNDAMENTAL IDEAS

This volume reports on research aimed at analysing these problems on a European scale, investigated initially from the perspectives of France, Germany, the Netherlands, Portugal and the United Kingdom.[1] This research involves three main thrusts:

- Obtaining a better definition of the nature and extent of flood threats on a European scale.
- Investigating policy responses to these threats, and evaluating best practices in different countries to inform policy development elsewhere.
- Overlaying both of these with some predictions about the effect of climate change on both the threats and the necessary responses.

We have conceptualised this research in the form of a diagram: Figure 1.1. This sees floods as events occurring as a result of both physical systems – the rainfall, rivers and coastal storms – and the human systems that are at risk and which themselves represent our uses of those riverine and coastal areas that are liable to flooding. The physical systems create hazardous impacts on our human systems, which in turn respond with attempts to manage and control both of these systems.

This conceptualisation is an adaptation of the classic hazard response theory developed by Gilbert White and his colleagues (e.g. Burton *et al.* 1978). This theory sees natural hazards as expressions of an imbalance in our relations with the environment in which we live. That imbalance can only be corrected by human action; it is not the environment that is 'at fault'.

Our conceptualisation also includes a climatic dimension. We can predict that both the hazardous impacts and the management and control dimensions of our model will need to change as climate change across Europe changes the nature of flood risks. Further into the future the picture is dimmer, but what continues is the essentially

---

1. The research is also being expanded to include Spain and Italy.

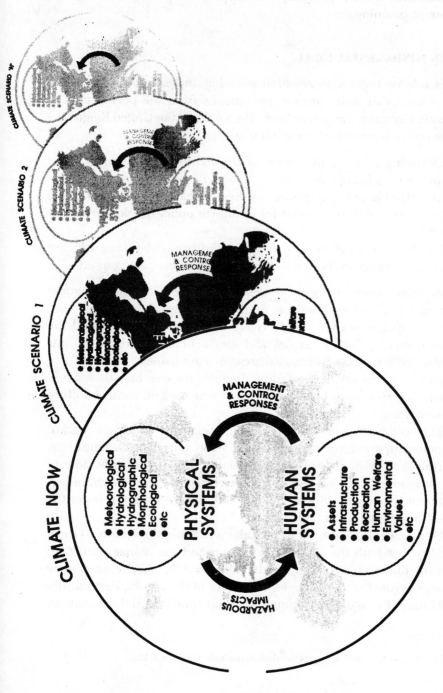

Figure 1.1: Physical systems and human systems interacting: our theoretical framework of hazard assessment, modelling and management.

dialectical relationship between the threats that are posed and the need for policy response.

THE FLOOD THREATS WE FACE: WHAT SHOULD BE DONE?

We know a great deal about the way that floods can be minimised, and the impacts of floods reduced. Research and development over many decades and centuries has identified what can be done, and when and where (Penning-Rowsell *et al.* 1986, Saul 1992).

A useful summary of this knowledge is shown in Figure 1.2. This shows, in the centre, the many different strategies that can be adopted to reduce the incidence and impacts of floods. The left-hand column shows these categorised, conventionally, as either structural solutions – generally involving engineering works – or non-structural approaches.

The right-hand side of Figure 1.2 is more interesting. This shows that each strategy can be seen as one of three types: measures to control the water that produces the flood (e.g. dams, reservoirs and sea defence dikes), measures to control vulnerability by controlling the use of land liable to flooding (e.g. planning controls on new development), or measures to distribute the losses from floods (e.g. through insurance schemes). This neatly matches our view that floods are not just physical phenomena; they are the result of our decisions to use the areas liable to flooding, and their impacts can be modified by the way in which we deploy the financial resources of our individuals and the state.

In the coastal environment, the policy options are slightly different; but they still emphasise decisions about how we use the areas that are under threat. Coastal areas can be the subject of threats from erosion and flooding and these are often interconnected: erosion can lead to flooding, which itself can cause erosion and lead to further flooding. The type of flooding and erosion that occurred at the coast in the past has traditionally led to a range of policy options based around defending the land against the threats from the sea. However, the current situation in Europe – and beyond – is, of course, compounded by the threat of sea-level rise consequent upon climate change.

This more complex situation can lead to the need for other types of policy to counter the threat and the hazards that could occur (Figure 1.3). There are three main options: first, 'holding the line' at

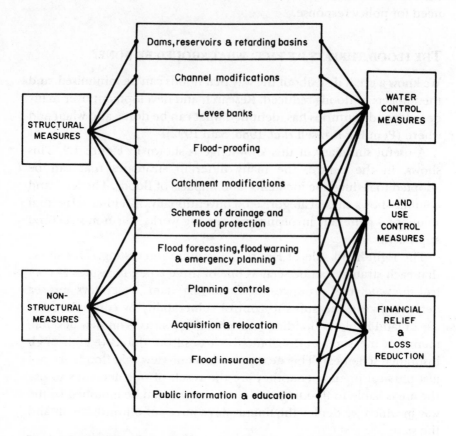

Figure 1.2: Alternative flood alleviation strategies: listing the solutions is simple; it is the implementation that brings the problems.

the current coast and shore line; secondly, 'managed retreat' to some other defendable line farther inland; and, thirdly, the 'walk away' option. This last, whereby the threat is not countered but allowed to have its impacts, involves finding a 'natural' shore line position between the sea and the land which balances the advantages of coastal protection to society against the impacts of the threat from the sea. This is akin to 'unmanaged retreat' and effectively is the 'do nothing' option.

So we know what can be done about the floods that we face from our rivers and at the coast; that is the easy bit. What is less simple is

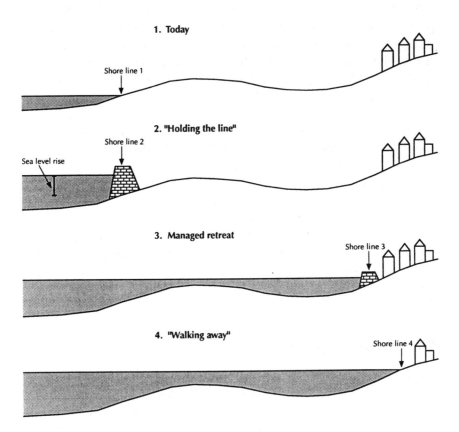

Figure 1.3: Policy options at the coast given sea-level rise consequent upon climate change: 'holding the line', 'managed retreat' and 'walking away'.

what will be done, and when and how. The problems arise with the implementation of sensible plans to reduce the risk and minimise the impacts (Izard 1972). It is in the conundrum of the simplicity of the solutions and the complexity of implementation that the fascination of our topic lies.

Floods, after all, are periodic events. In between these events, people forget their impacts because they are otherwise engaged in the day-to-day processes of their personal and social lives. There are more important things to think of for most people most of the time than the floods that might affect them next winter, or when the next storm comes.

So after the initial clamour following a serious flood, when the newspapers have turned their attention elsewhere, the pressure to 'do something' can wane, particularly in those many cases where it is the poor and weak in society that suffer the floods since they occupy the cheap land that traditionally has had those flood problems. Public money becomes harder to find. The disruption of treasured historic river and coastal sites by engineering works is resisted. Non-structural solutions are hard to implement, since they often involve complex interagency cooperation and power sharing – such as in the development of flood forecasts and the dissemination of flood warnings. Delay is a powerful political weapon, whether used consciously or unconsciously.

The result can be inaction. So the flood threat continues, or grows, and generally it is only a major event that stimulates the political processes necessary to see the implementation of a sensibly comprehensive approach to flood alleviation. The randomness of this political process means, in turn, that the imbalance that White and his colleagues describe is more likely to be the case than not; we live dangerously.

THE SPECIAL EUROPEAN DIMENSION

So that is the framework. Now what is the European dimension? What is the European analysis of flood hazards that is different from the national or the local analysis? How, moreover, does our investigation of flood hazards on a national scale benefit from the European context to the questions that we ask? Does it help?

The question of scale

First, there is the question of scale. A European scale of analysis forces us to concentrate on the large European-scale threats and floods that have national and international significance. We know, of course, that more people are affected by the purely local flood events, which may be a product of locally poor urban drainage or the flooding from a local rural stream. But it is the major events that should concern national governments and international agencies such as the European Commission. Here there is the potential for major damage to our assets and investments, and also for the disruption of key communications. Tackling these hazards can require transnational cooperation, resources and emergency planning.

Flood potential on this scale exists all over Europe, such as in the diked area of the Netherlands; the east coast of Britain; the north German coastal plain; the Rhine, Seine and Loire valleys; the coastal areas of Portugal; and the lower Po valley in Italy. These are among the economic heartlands of the European Union, rich in assets and productive capacity. Major damage and dislocation here would affect the fabric and economies of the countries that contain them, and even disturb the European scene. And yet this is despite decades or even centuries of investment in river and coastal management works; the problems continue to arise, to surprise and alarm us.

The Union of different states

But the European dimension also emphasises, secondly, another aspect of flood hazard mitigation: the varying social and economic dimension within the countries of the European Union.

Central to policy comparison here is the way in which different countries control the use of their land, including land in areas liable to flooding. Our diagnosis of flood problems includes a conclusion that at least part of the problem – and the dominant factor in many areas – is urban encroachment into areas that naturally carry flood waters. We are building vulnerability into our developments by locating them in areas of flood risk. This points to the need for land use controls, which necessitates a knowledge of land use law, planning decisions and the nature of power and influence over such matters.

Here there are striking European contrasts. For some countries the need for land use controls has only been recognised relatively recently – as in Portugal and Italy. In others, such controls are seen as an unwelcome intrusion into the freedom of land owners to exploit the land resources that they own. In yet other countries – such as the Netherlands and the United Kingdom – the tradition of land use planning goes back at least fifty years and in many cases much longer, but newly constructed houses and factories are still flooded there. This shows that all may not be well.

In addition, the legal traditions of the countries – and whether they are the legal 'code' countries or those where common law dominates – will affect attitudes towards river and coastal zone management and its enforcement. In turn these legal traditions affect our analysis and our recommendations for tackling the flood hazards that we face. Across the different countries of Europe – and the sub-set of the ones that we are so far studying in depth – these differences are well illustrated. They affect the way that we must research and analyse the policies that exist and the improvements that we can recommend for the future.

Different legal traditions and other factors have also led to different administrative and political systems. These can affect flood hazard mitigation by influencing the flow of resources and also the way in which communication and decision-making systems are structured for use at times of hazard and warning dissemination.

Thus some countries, such as Germany, have a federal system, whereas other countries have other forms of devolution – a process that is currently actively under way in Italy and has been implemented in France. The United Kingdom has quite different arrangements in Scotland from those in England and Wales, and Northern Ireland is different again. These differences can affect our governments' perception of flooding as a local, regional or national problem, and also the way in which responses are organised and delivered.

Economic circumstances also affect attitudes to floods and their impacts. The damage potential from floods in the Netherlands is large even in relation to the high gross national product there, but national experience in the 1953 floods dictates that flood mitigation should be given top priority. In other countries – perhaps those that are less developed within Europe – it is the imperative of economic development that determines the use of flood-prone areas, particularly if they are adjacent to expanding urban settlements. Here the policy may be to build on the flood plain areas and worry about the flooding later, which is unwise but understandable.

The climatic scene

Thirdly, Europe encompasses a wide range of climatic conditions, from 36 degrees North at the southernmost point of Spain, to 60 degrees North at the Shetland Islands, north of Scotland. Annual rainfall varies between just over 300 mm in eastern Spain, to up to 3,000 mm in areas of the Alps and western Scotland. Areas of southern Europe have local climates that include regular and serious summer thunderstorms, whereas areas of western Europe can suffer from heavy frontal rainfalls over many days or weeks, carried there by Atlantic depressions formed at the interface between tropical and Arctic airstreams.

To complicate matters, the different national climates will probably react differently to climate change. Increased storminess will have most impact in those areas which are currently the more stable. The effect on fluvial run-off is far from clear, but it is likely that there will be different impacts in areas with different fluvial characteristics, such as inland Germany or coastal Spain. Sea-level rise consequent upon climate change will affect some countries more than others.

These different types of meteorological conditions across Europe mean that different flood circumstances can be expected in different areas. This adds depth to our analysis and emphasises the complexity of policy development. There are no simple answers, hence the interest in the subject.

Harmonisation and 'subsidiarity'

But in the midst of this differentiation there is the European Union and its moves towards harmonisation and standardisation. This can be overstressed, but the Union involves a continuous political and economic 'push' towards this harmonisation, promoted ultimately through the Treaties of Rome and Maastricht and the impacts that these have on national legislation. This process in turn has resulted in European Union directives in water and related fields which seek standardisation and probably indicate the future direction of policy development.

Thus the increasing amount of European environmental regulation seeks to harmonise the approach to environmental standards, public sector investment appraisal and land use change, particularly through the use of environmental impact assessment. Also, the concepts of sustainable development have been accepted by the countries of the Union. Although it is yet to be seen how these will be worked out in the future management of our rivers and the protection of coasts and wetlands, it is likely that moves will be towards policy harmonisation rather than away from it.

The European Commission certainly wishes to see such harmonisation, but it also recognises the expressions of national autonomy and pressures therein for 'subsidiarity' that will mean the retention of national differences. It is the interplay between these tendencies that will be worked out at a number of policy levels in the future, and in the hazard mitigation field – just as in other areas – there are costs and benefits from standardisation across the different conditions that are currently experienced in Europe.

The benefits for research: the comparative dimension

But how, then, does our investigation of flood hazards on a national scale benefit from the European context? At least four points are important here.

First, a European perspective challenges national ideas, conventions and policies by providing counter-suggestions from elsewhere. For example, flood mitigation standards are different in different countries, and national traditions – such as the primacy of flood alleviation in the Netherlands – create circumstances which challenge the practices elsewhere.

Secondly, different nations are at different stages of policy development, and there are therefore role models to follow. A European scale of analysis can mean that mistakes are minimised by those seeking to improve their hazard mitigation policies, through taking advantage of the lessons learned the hard way by others.

Thirdly, the research traditions and emphases in the flood hazard field in the different countries are different. This means that a European analysis of research results and policy implications is inherently richer than can be obtained on a purely national scale.

Fourthly, our research can benefit from the analysis of transboundary issues, particularly with respect to international rivers such as the Rhine and Duoro and coastal zone areas crossing state boundaries – for example, the zone between France, Belgium and the Netherlands. Our European scale of analysis means that international issues cannot be ignored, and emphasises the need to have a measure of consistency in analysis, methods, models and policies across these boundaries if flood problems are to be tackled adequately.

THE NATURE OF THE PROBLEM: A TENTATIVE TYPOLOGY OF EUROPEAN FLOOD HAZARDS

The 1993–4 floods in Europe – France, the Netherlands, Germany, the United Kingdom – caused substantial damages to private and public property, enormous social disruption, and sporadic loss of life. In the Netherlands, the flood in the south of the country in December 1993 led to the area being officially declared a national disaster. The damage assessed so far by loss adjusters, working for the government to decide on levels of financial compensation, amounted to the equivalent of 100 million ECUs.

In Germany, in Bonn, the new parliamentary building which is under construction has been undermined by flooding, again causing significant damage. In the United Kingdom, the town of Chichester was significantly affected by flooding for well over a week, causing damage and dislocation. Almost every day during December 1993 and January 1994 across Europe television news brought pictures of floating cars, collapsed bridges and demolished houses.

So what is the nature of the problem that we are addressing? How serious is the flood hazard situation in Europe and, in turn, in the different countries and environments there represented?

We cannot yet answer those questions definitively for all countries, although the information on which to base answers is growing all the time. Our collaborative research programme is working on a definitive typology of floods and flood threats, and assessing the extent of these problems in the different countries of the European Union. To this end we have developed an initial typology which is being assessed across Europe. The aim is to devise a system that is simple in the number of categories that it contains but at the same time comprehensive in including all the types of floods that occur in the areas concerned.

The eight main types of flooding and flood risk in Europe are described briefly below.

Winter rainfall floods

Westerly depressions with well-developed warm fronts bring winter precipitation which – when heavy, continuous and prolonged – can lead to natural soils becoming saturated, in turn leading to high volumes of run-off. When this occurs rivers may flow out of bank, causing flooding which can be serious if the rainfall is very prolonged and catchments were previously saturated. Flooding in England in 1994 was an example of this type of flooding, which followed a December during which four times the monthly December average rainfall fell.

Snowmelt floods

Rapid snowmelt in changeable weather conditions is sometimes an important contributory cause in this type of flooding. This is most likely to occur in spring, when warm southern airstreams track north-wards into Alpine or upland areas, creating sudden snowmelt accom-panied sometimes by heavy rainfall. This phenomenon can be very localised and when this is the case and urban areas occupy valley bottoms, the effects can be serious, especially since flood water velocities can be high. This was the case with the floods that affected Perth in Scotland in 1993.

Summer convectional storm induced floods

Intensive storms and floods are sometimes caused by convectional thunderstorms. These usually occur in summer months and appear to have become more frequent over heavily urbanised areas where the urban 'heat island' effect is pronounced. They also can be common in southern European areas where prolonged hot periods of the summer months can end with sudden storms. The floods in France in 1992 in Vaison-la-Romaine are an example of this type of problem, which has also occurred in the coastal streams adjacent to Lisbon in Portugal. The seriousness of this type of flooding is compounded by the fact that coastal and other flood plain areas can be in seasonal use for camp sites and the like in the areas affected.

Sewer flooding

Many of our older cities have inadequate sewerage systems, which means that normal intensive rainfall events can create abnormal flooding. Some new developments in Europe also have inadequate storm sewer systems because the developments are unplanned – or even illegal – settlements. Whilst this problem can be locally serious, this type of flooding is more likely to be a nagging minor problem when viewed on a continental scale.

Urban basement flooding

In some urban areas a basement flooding problem has emerged in recent years due to the rise in the water table associated with in-dustrial and urban decline that has itself led to a decline in the number of water abstractions from boreholes in these areas. The ground water levels rise, emerging in basement areas as permanent waterlogging. Again, this is a small localised problem rather than a serious hazard.

Lowland waterlogging

High levels of water retention in lowland clay soils, together with low evapotranspiration rates in the cool, moist climate, result in waterlogging and flooding in many parts of lowland Europe. Areas can be flooded because rainfall in areas surrounded by embankments fails to find an outflow. Many lowland areas can be flooded for weeks or months, but in these areas agricultural practice has tended to respond, and water-resistant and low-value crops are generally grown.

Sea surge and tidal flood threat

Sea and tidal flooding is a major problem – and the largest threat to life – and it is closely bound to the problem of coastal erosion which may subsequently lead to flooding. Many European coastal areas are low lying and the main threat is from a combination of high tides, low atmospheric pressure and strong onshore winds producing tidal surges. Coastal flooding can also arise. from other mechanisms, including seepage of sea water at high tide through natural shingle embankments, through artificial banks created to protect land from the sea, through breaches of these embankments, and occasionally through ocean swell phenomena – perhaps related to earthquake activity in the mid-Atlantic ridge area, causing waves to overtop these embankments. Secular sea-level rise, isostatic land-level fall and local land subsidence are all problems which add to tidal and sea flooding problems. The floods in 1953 in the Netherlands and the United Kingdom are an example of this type of problem.

Dam-break flood risk

Finally, there are low probability/high consequence flood risks associated with some of the many large dams which have been constructed in Europe, some of them many years ago. There is a low probability seismic hazard which could trigger dam-breaks under certain conditions (Bossman-Aggrey et al. 1987). Clearly any floods that have this cause are likely to be very serious.

There is, with all these types of floods, a certain seasonality implied. The main flood season in most northerly European states, therefore, is the winter period from October to March, when westerly depressions bring storms and rainfall. It is during this period that most riverine, tidal and sea floods occur, such as the major flood on the

Rhine in 1993. Springtime can bring floods resulting from rapid snowmelt. The summer months are often associated with convectional storms and sudden intense flooding throughout any part of Europe but especially in heavily urbanised areas and coastal regions in the south of Europe. Other types of flooding may also have seasonal characteristics (e.g. dam-break floods, basement flooding and sewer surcharge tend to be winter phenomena) but may occur in either the winter or summer.

OUR RESEARCH[2]

In the chapters that follow we give the results of our research, set within the multi-faceted framework that this chapter has described.

Thus in Chapter 2 we look at the state of our knowledge of possible climate change, as a backdrop to our research on flood impacts and responses. In Chapter 3 we examine two important and related themes. The first is the type and extent of the impact that floods have on people, drawing mainly on case studies in the United Kingdom but also using material from France. The second is the nature of decision-making concerning public investment in flood alleviation and coastal management strategies, and in particular how to incorporate the many 'intangible' dimensions into these decisions. This analysis uses material from the United Kingdom and the Netherlands.

Chapter 4 then reviews the development of computer models to assess the magnitude of flood impacts analysed at the regional or larger scale suitable for a European perspective. This draws on conceptual modelling and on application work in Germany, which itself is founded on earlier research in the Netherlands and the United Kingdom. Also at a large scale is the analysis of flood dike safety standards in the Netherlands described in Chapter 5; this is set clearly in the context of the impacts there of climate change and the likely sea-level rise.

In Chapters 6 and 7 we look at policy development and implementation. In the first of these we look at how flood warning systems are developing in a European context, with results from detailed and

---

2. The summary of the research given in this volume is complemented by a series of technical annexes giving the research results in much greater detail. These are available from Middlesex University or one of the partner research teams.

comparative policy analysis in the United Kingdom, the Netherlands, France, Portugal and Germany. In Chapter 7 we look at the way that the planning of flood alleviation schemes tackles the political dimension: how the interface with the public is analysed and managed, with reference mainly to the United Kingdom and Portugal. In the final chapter – Chapter 8 – we evaluate our key research conclusions and review their implications at both a national and an international scale.

So what is our aim? We hope, through these chapters (and their separately published technical annexes) to combine, first, a meaningful and detailed study of real floods and real policy dilemmas in the different countries with, secondly, the development of a Europe-wide framework for better hazard assessment and policy implementation in the future. Serious scientific analysis is our method; realistic policy enhancement is our goal.

REFERENCES

Bossman-Aggrey, P.; Parker, D.J. and Green, C.H. (1987) *Dam Safety Management in the United Kingdom.* Middlesex University School of Geography and Planning Paper no. 21. London, UK: Middlesex University, Flood Hazard Research Centre

Burton, I.; Kates, R. and White, G. (1978) *The Environment as Hazard.* New York, USA: Oxford University Press

Izard, I. (1972) *Ecological-economic Analysis for Regional Development.* New York, USA: The Free Press

Penning-Rowsell, E.C.; Parker, D.J. and Harding, D.M. (1986) *Floods and Drainage: British policies for hazard reduction, agricultural improvement and wetland conservation.* London, UK: Allen and Unwin

Saul, A.J. (ed.) (1992) *Floods and Flood Management.* Dordrecht, Netherlands: Kluwer Academic Publishers

CHAPTER 2

The Risks We Face: Climate Change and Future Flood Threats

Gerard Hesselmans and Bart Peerbolte

INTRODUCTION

As explained in Chapter 1, we are seeking in this volume to evaluate the nature of the hazard presented by flooding on the European scale, with all the complexities thereby involved. These complexities include the nature of the data we use, the models employed for predicting the future, and the dilemmas posed by uncertainty for decision making about the requirement for policy change.

Central to debates about the nature of floods that Europe faces is the possibility of climate change, and changes therefore to both sea levels and river discharges. Although uncertainties abound in these fields, we have collated the best and most recent information available on these topics here, so as to present a context for subsequent chapters on the nature of flood hazard modelling and the appropriate policy responses. As such this chapter draws heavily upon published work, particularly that emanating from the Intergovernmental Panel on Climate Change (IPCC). This panel has been in the forefront of developing data sets and the compilation of models for assessing the possible impact of climate change, and national agencies and regional institutions – including European institutions – have been central to developing parts of this work and producing reports summarising their results.

In the late 1980s several reports were thus published on climate change and sea-level rise. Well known examples are 'The Scientific Assessment for the Intergovernmental Panel on Climate Change' (IPCC 1990) and, on the Dutch national scene, Technical Report 6 on sea-level rise and coastal defence after 1990 (Ronde and Vogel 1988) prepared for the Dutch government in 1988. These reports present the state of the art at that time. Since then some insights have changed owing to the availability of better and more observations and more advanced climate models.

Our aim here is to present the most recent findings with respect to climate change. New results can be found, for example in the work of Wigley and Raper (1992). To assess the latest findings two experts in this field, namely Professor J. Oerlemans and Professor C.J.E. Schuurmans, were also consulted. They are based respectively at the Institute for Marine and Atmospheric Research at the University of Utrecht and the Royal Netherlands Meteorological Institute (KNMI). They are specialists in melting of ice on glaciers and at the poles, and on climate and circulation.

This chapter will therefore consider the different contributions to sea-level rise and other climate effects related to global temperature changes. First, historical data will be presented; these are needed to calibrate numerical models and to prove the existence of the 'greenhouse effect'. Then, secondly, results of model predictions for the near future will be presented and discussed. Finally, conclusions will be drawn as to the implications of these results.

HISTORICAL INFORMATION

At many locations all over the world data concerning the local hydrological and meteorological conditions have been collected. However, the quality of these data is often limited: time sequences are interrupted for several years and measuring methodology has changed and so on. The most reliable results are available only for temperature and sea water levels and these are considered below.

Global mean temperature

Current estimates of smoothed global mean surface temperature over land and the oceans since 1860 are shown in Figure 2.1. Although the overall temperature rise has been broadly similar in both hemispheres, it has not been steady and differences in the rates of warming have sometimes persisted for decades. Much of the warming since 1900 was concentrated in two periods, the first period between

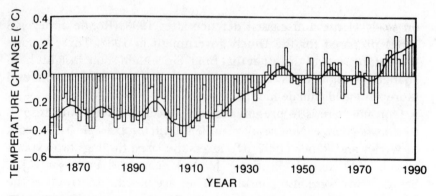

Figure 2.1: Global mean combined land-air and sea-surface temperatures, 1861–1989, relative to the average for 1951–80 (source IPCC 1990, figure 11, pp xxix).

about 1910 and 1940 and the second from 1975; the seven warmest years on record have occurred since 1980.

Average warming over parts of the northern hemisphere mid-latitude continents has been found to be largely characterised by increases in minimum (night-time) rather than maximum (day-time) temperatures. The northern hemisphere cooled between the 1940s and the early 1970s, whereas southern hemisphere temperatures remained nearly constant. Changes in surface temperature in different regions of the two hemispheres have shown considerable contrasts for periods as long as decades throughout the last hundred years, notably in the northern hemisphere. This regional diversity indicates that future regional temperature changes are likely to differ considerably from a global average.

Sea water levels

Historical evidence for relative sea-level rise can be found in the tidal records of Dutch harbours. Data over the last one hundred years are presented in Table 2.1 (Ronde and Vogel 1988, Dillingh 1992).

The trend in the average low and high water levels on the Dutch coast does not follow the trend in the relative sea level. Only 5 per cent of the increase in water levels can be explained by sea-level rise (Ronde and Vogel 1988). The trend in the average low and high water levels can better be explained by changes in the tidal range. The increase in the tidal range can in the main be attributed to human activity (Langendoen 1987): the deepening of channels, harbour constructions, the Delta works and so on. The effect of human activity

Table 2.1: Changes in relative sea level compared with average low and high water levels over the period 1940–90 for several harbours in the Netherlands (cm per century)

	Relative sea-level rise 1900-1990	Relative sea-level rise 1940-1990	Increase in average high water 1940-1990	Increase in average low water 1940-1990	Increase in tidal range 1940-1990
Vlissingen	23	19	29	15	14
Hoek van Holland	26	28	(44)	22	(22)
Ijmuiden	21	20	32	16	16
Den Helder	17	20	22	12	10
Harlingen	16	19	31	14	17
Terschelling	16	11	28	-1	29
Delfzijl	21	23	(49)	(-10)	(60)

() = there is no uniform trend

can be eliminated by considering changes in water levels during the recent period without major human interfering activity. Thus analysed, changes in sea-level rise tend to be more uniform than the changes presented in Table 2.1; the average increase turns out to be 19 cm per century, but since additional coastal works will be executed in the future it is very difficult to give estimates of expected future changes. Increasing tidal ranges are also found along the Belgian and German coasts, but not along the British coast.

Ronde and Heinen (1993) have analysed the changes in the tide gauge records along the Dutch coast (see Table 2.1). This analysis shows that 75 per cent of the variance can be explained by the trend, 11 per cent by air pressure and 0.06 per cent by the nodal tide, leaving 14 per cent for 'noise'. A comparison of the first two columns of Table 2.1 shows that the increase in relative sea-level rise over the period 1940–90 is 2 cm higher than the increase over 1901–86. However, taking the above hydro-meteorological conditions into account (air pressure and nodal tide), no additional increase in relative mean sea-level rise over the last years is observed for the Dutch coast.

MODEL PREDICTIONS OF SEA-LEVEL RISE

To carry out a climate forecast it is necessary to take into account the complex interactions and feedback systems between the different components of the climate system. This is done through the use of a numerical model which includes, as far as possible, a description of all the processes and interactions involved.

The most elaborate climate model employed at present consists of an atmospheric global circulation model (GCM) coupled to an ocean GCM which describes the structure and dynamics of the ocean. Added to this coupled model are appropriate descriptions – although these are necessarily somewhat crude – of the other components of the climate system; namely, the land surface and the ice formations, and the interactions between them. If the model is run for several years with parameters and forcing appropriate to the current climate, the model's output should bear a close resemblance to the observed climate. If parameters representing, say, an increasing amount of greenhouse gases are introduced into the model, it can be used to simulate or predict the resulting climate change.

The IPCC 1990 report shows a fair measure of agreement between the different climate models which are in use over the world, as far as an average global temperature rise is concerned. In general the expected increase in global temperature depends on the selected scenario. A scenario is characterised by a set of parameters describing, for example, the annual emission of the greenhouse gas carbon dioxide, held to be responsible for 50 per cent of the greenhouse effect.

Most studies use at least three scenarios: 'Business-as-usual', low emission (favourable) and high emission (unfavourable). When the TR6 1988 and the IPCC 1990 reports were published the expected rate of increase in global mean temperature during the next century was about 0.3° C per decade, using the Business-as-usual scenario. For the high and low emission scenarios the expected temperature changes are 0.2° C and 0.5° C respectively. Based on more recent results these predictions have been lowered to 1.7° C, 2.5° C and 3.8° C per century (IPCC 1992, Wigley and Raper 1992).

Model predictions have been changed due, first, to improvements in climate models with regard to physical realism. Models now include the effects of stratospheric-ozone-depletion feedback, sulphate aerosols and the terrestrial biosphere. Due to these feedback effects the radiative forcing reduces by about 20 to 25 per cent (Figure 2.2). Furthermore, new techniques for the simulation of regional climates have been introduced. Secondly, there have been changes in the scenarios, principally concerned with changes in population forecasts, the availability of renewable energy sources, tropical deforestation and forest biomass content and so on.

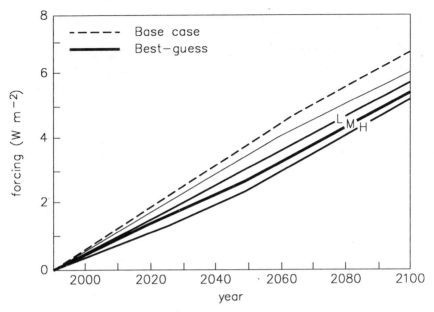

Figure 2.2: Radiative forcing projection for emission scenario IS92a. The base case is IPCC 1990 scenario (no feedback). The effect of CO_2 fertilisation feedback and ozone-depletion feedback is represented by the curve just below the base curve. L, M and H refer to low, middle and high aerosol forcing possibilities (adapted from Wigley and Raper 1992).

Sea-level rise

Given the expected change in global temperature, the effect of the individual components on sea-level rise can be assessed. These are melting of glaciers, thermal expansion of the oceans, changes in the amount of ice at the North Pole, changes in the Greenland ice sheet and changes in the Antarctic ice sheet. For the low-lying countries local subsidence (the lowering of the ground surface due to sinking, compaction and consolidation of deep subsoils) is important as well. For the Netherlands a lowering of 4 to 8 cm is expected.

With respect to the melting of glaciers, the majority of valley glaciers have been retreating over the last hundred years. The total amount of water stored in these mountain glaciers (excluding Greenland, Antarctic and the North Pole) is equivalent in sea-level rise terms to 50 to 60 cm. It is estimated that the melting of glaciers has caused a sea-level rise of 2 to 6 cm over the last century. In Oerlemans and Fortuin (1992) it is concluded that the sensitivity of glaciers and small ice caps to greenhouse warming has been overestimated until now. According to Oerlemans (1993) the best estimate for this melting of glaciers is now some 12.6 cm sea-level rise per century.

The thermal expansion of the oceans could be much more important. At constant mass, the volume of the oceans, and thus the sea level, will vary with changes in the density of sea water. As oceans warm up, the density decreases and the oceans will expand. Oceanic expansion strongly depends on the yet unknown speed of heating of the oceans, stratification effects and water circulation. It is estimated that due to thermal expansion the sea level has risen 2 to 8 cm over the last hundred years; another 20 to 40 cm increase is expected in the next century.

With regard to the North Pole and Greenland ice sheets, the ice sheet at the North Pole floats and even if it melts completely it will not result in any sea-level rise. The mass budget of the Greenland ice sheet is affected by melting and precipitation (snowfall). Owing to the greenhouse effect, the maximum percentage of atmospheric moisture will increase, which may result in more precipitation. It is expected that the increased melting will dominate the increase in precipitation, resulting in a sea-level rise of 0 to 10 cm in the next hundred years.

Melting of ice in Antarctica is of minor importance, because the continent is too cold. The discharge of ice is mainly caused by the breaking off of ice sheets and the crumbling of glaciers. Owing to a rise in mean temperature, humidity and precipitation in the Antarctic are expected to increase, and therefore the process of snowfall will be most significant and a sea-level decrease is to be expected. The current estimates range from 0 to 5 cm. Huybrechts and Oerlemans (1990) predict that the effect of increased snow and ice accumulation due to precipitation will outweigh the increase in run-off, as long as the temperature increase remains below 5.3° C.

Wind climate

Mid-latitude storms are driven by the equator-to-pole temperature gradient. This gradient will probably be weakened in a warmer world, at least in the northern hemisphere. Therefore, it might be argued that mid-latitude storms will also weaken or change their tracks. Indeed there is some indication of a general reduction in day-to-day variability in the mid-latitude storm tracks in winter in storm simulations. Current models, however, do not resolve at scales to pick up these smaller-scale disturbances, so it will not be possible to assess changes in storminess until results from higher resolution models become available.

Precipitation

Models to simulate precipitation are able to predict the broad features of the observed patterns, with useful regional detail in some regions. However, significant errors are present. Depending on the model, the mean magnitude varies from 20 to 50 per cent of the observed values.

Equilibrium studies on precipitation show that if the CO_2 concentration doubles, then the global average precipitation will increase (as does that of evaporation); the larger the warming, the larger the increase. Also there will be an increase in precipitation at high latitudes throughout the year, and precipitation will increase globally by 3 to 15 per cent (as does evaporation); finally, an increase in precipitation will occur at mid-latitudes in winter.

Regional climate change

Regional climate changes are likely to be different from the global mean, although our confidence in the prediction of the detail of regional changes is low. For the two mid-latitude areas the following results are presented for changes by the year 2030 (IPCC 1990).

In southern Europe (35°–50° N; 10°–45° E) the warming is about 2° C in winter and varies from 2° C to 3° C in summer. There is some indication of increased precipitation in winter (0 to 10 per cent), but summer precipitation decreases by 5 to 15 per cent, and summer soil moisture falls by 15 to 25 per cent.

In central North America (35°–50° N; 85°–105° W) the warming varies from 2° C to 4° C in winter and 2 to 3° C in summer. Precipitation increases range from 0 to 15 per cent in winter, whereas decreases of 5 to 10 per cent may occur in summer. Soil moisture decreases in summer by 15 to 20 per cent.

The global mean temperature rise for the northern hemisphere at the time of CO_2 doubling is expected to be between 1.5° C and 5.5° C (Toetsing uitgangspunten rivierdijkversterkingen 1993). The regional temperature changes for Europe are presented in Table 2.2. In view of the large uncertainties in the average global temperature rise, the values presented should only be taken as an indication of the relative changes.

Table 2.2: Expected season-averaged temperature increase in ° C for Europe according to the USO–GCM scenario.

Region	Winter	Spring	Summer	Autumn
Boreal and subarctic	5-8	3-4	2-3	3
Atlantic	3-4	3	3	3
Continental	4-5	3	4	3
Mediterranean	3-4	3	3	3

The trend of the changes in precipitation is still unclear for Europe and may even be opposite for different countries in the European Union. However, there is a general trend in the predicted changes in climates in northern and southern Europe: the southern part will become relatively dryer, whereas the northern part will become relatively warmer.

Regional differences in sea level occur owing to ocean circulation and atmospheric pressure differences. At present differences due to geostrophic currents are about 2 m. Church *et al.* (1991) predict additional regional differences by the year 2050 of less than about 0.1 m due to global warming of 3° C, whereas the Max Planck Institute at Hamburg predicts an additional sea-level rise of 15 cm for northern Europe as compared with the global mean.

River discharges and climate change

Kwadijk (1991) studied the sensitivity of the discharge of the River Rhine to climate changes and changes in land use. The effect of two scenarios has been assessed. The first is for a change in the rain/snow precipitation pattern due to a temperature increase of 4° C in the Alpine part of the river basin. This will result in a reduction of 10 to 15 per cent in discharge at Lobith (in the Netherlands) in summer. The second scenario is for a large-scale change in land use in the German/French part of the river basin (including urbanisation and retention basins) which, assuming no change in climate, will result in reduced evapotranspiration and an annual discharge at Lobith reduced by 9 to 10 per cent. It should be emphasised that these possible changes are due to the changes in a single parameter. The combined effect of several parameters changing may be considerably larger.

Kwadijk and Middelkoop (1992) have related the average monthly discharge to the peak discharge of the Rhine basin. This enables them to predict peak discharges. Assuming an increase in temperature of 2° C and a 10 per cent reduction in precipitation, a critical discharge of $Q_{t=1250} = 14{,}300$ m³/s is anticipated. Based on extreme value statistics applied to historical data (for 1901–90) the critical discharge is $Q_{t=1250} = 15{,}000$ m³/s. Therefore, due to climate changes, a reduction of 700 m³/s is expected. In view of the large uncertainty in the temperature/precipitation climate scenarios, Kwadijk estimates that $Q_{t=1250}$ could be as much as 4500 m³/s lower or 2000 m³/s higher.

More detailed river discharge analyses are not possible at present, because of the grid size of the GCMs currently used. The whole drainage basin of a large European river such as the Rhine fits into just one or two grid cells.

Trends

Most authors estimate model parameters by matching model results and historical data. Oerlemans uses best estimates of these parameters based on physical models. The remaining error is included in a trend. This trend may not only describe parameter errors but may also account for effects not yet included in the models. The latter approach makes it possible to make a distinction between the contributions to sea-level rise which we currently understand and the part which is not yet understood. The results are given in Figure 2.3.

CONCLUSIONS AND ASSESSMENT

Since the publication of the TR6 and IPCC reports, estimates of sea-level rise have changed as new insight has arisen. This is summarised in Table 2.3. It should be noted that some values presented there are based on taking information from the chronologically previous report (i.e. values in the next column to the left, on the same line), by means of extrapolation or interpolation, and they should be treated as best-guess values.

Much uncertainty therefore remains in the prediction of global climate properties such as temperature and rainfall. Even greater uncertainty exists in predictions of regional climate change, and the subsequent consequences for sea level, precipitation, wind climate, wave climate and ecosystems. Hindcast studies show that the GCMs used today yield results which may be strongly biased. Unfortunately bias is largest over Europe. Because the model results are still

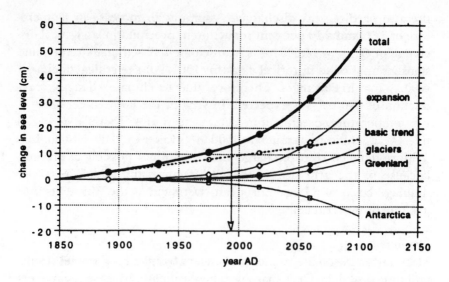

Figure 2.3: Global change in sea level (cm) as predicted by Oerlemans (1993).

Table 2.3: Contributions to sea-level rise.

	TR6 1988	IPCC 1990	IPCC 1992	Wigley 1992	Oerlemans 1993
Global temperature rise	3.0	3.0	2.5	2.5	2.5
Melting of glaciers	20.0	23.3	23.3	20.2	12.6
North Pole	0.0	0.0	0.0	0.0	0.0
Greenland ice sheet	5.0	6.0	6.0	5.2	7.9
Antarctic ice sheet	-2.0	-2.0	-2.0	-1.7	-13.6
Thermal expansion	30.0	33.7	33.7	24.3	30.7
trend (the Netherlands)					12.1
Sea-level rise	53.0	61.0	55.4	48.0	49.7
Bottom lowering (The Netherlands)	6.0	6.0	6.0	6.0	6.0
Relative sea-level rise	59	67.0	61.4	54.0	55.7

uncertain, Professor Schuurmans is of the opinion that trends in historical data are more useful. Professor Oerlemans estimates the uncertainty in the sea-level rise to be of the same order of magnitude as the expected rise.

Since the confidence in regional changes simulated by GCMs remains low, it is prudent not to exclude the possibility of unfavourable changes in wind speed or wind direction. Such changes are given in the TR6 (Ronde and Vogel 1988) report: they are for a 10 per cent increase in wind speed and a 10 degree change in wind direction. The same conclusion can be made with respect to the wave conditions: a 10 per cent increase in wave height and a 10 degree change in wave direction.

With respect to extreme water levels the conclusions of the Ronde and Vogel (1988) report are still valid. The prospective increase in average high water level is: sea-level rise +5 cm, and the increase in average low water level is: sea-level rise −5 cm.

Changes in the predicted river discharge of the River Rhine and other rivers are uncertain. For the River Rhine, models indicate a decreased critical discharge with a lower bound of minus 30 per cent and an upper bound of plus 15 per cent.

For the North Sea, where the flood threat in Europe from sea-level rise in the future is most obvious, improvements in predictions at a regional scale can only be made by reducing the grid spacing from the current models (±1000 km) to ±100 km. This can be achieved by nesting a regional model in a GCM. The GCM then gives the boundary conditions of the regional model. Boundaries should be selected where systematic errors of the GCM are small. Research along this line has been initiated in Europe and the first results are expected in the mid-1990s.

The general conclusion, therefore, is that for the time being there is no scientific evidence to reject the estimates given in 1988 in the TR6 report (Ronde and Vogel 1988). However, it should be borne in mind that in spite of the consensus about the greenhouse effect and associated climate changes, this scenario cannot be considered as a hard computational result. Indeed, although it is acknowledged that coupled atmosphere-ocean GCMs have improved, we believe that predictions about climate change are still as speculative as they were in 1988.

This conclusion poses considerable dilemmas for policy making. Programmes of investment in flood alleviation works, and coastal protection schemes designed to defend against both erosion and flooding, frequently take many years or decades to design and implement. Many other considerations are involved, other than the predictions of the nature of the hazard – including the environmental impact of any work, the financing of the schemes, and the relationships between any works and associated infrastructure (e.g. ports and harbours, recreational development, land drainage facilities). What we can see from this chapter is that there could be significant changes in sea levels as a result of climate change, and there might be increases in river discharges, although these latter seem unlikely. Further data and better models developed in the future may confirm these predictions, but it is possible that some decisions about future works to alleviate flooding may have to be made now, based on the necessarily crude current models and the inadequate data that we have today.

Therefore, as far as this volume is concerned, we necessarily have to assume that flooding problems in Europe will continue to be at least as serious as they are now, and that they could get worse. This means that we may need to build sensitivity analyses into the models that we are developing to predict the extent and nature of flood hazards (e.g. as described in Chapter 4), and governments may have to take decisions based on the precautionary principle, building in some contingency for possible climate change. These kinds of conclusions should form a context to our discussions in the next chapters about the nature of flood hazards and the appropriate policy responses.

REFERENCES

Church, J.A.; Godfrey, J.S.; Jackett, D.R. and McDougall, T.J. (1991) A Model of Sea Level Rise Caused by Ocean Thermal Expansion. *Journal of Climate,* 4

Commissie Rivierdijken (1977) *Rapport Commissie Rivierdijken.* The Hague, Netherlands: Ministerie van Verkeer en Waterstaat

Delft Hydraulics and the European American Center for Policy Analysis (EAC/RAND) (1993) *Examination of the Premises of the (Dutch) River Dike Strengthening Program.* Final report, and partial report 2: critical loads. The Hague, Netherlands: Ministerie van Verkeer en Waterstaat

Dillingh, D. (1992) *Zeespiegelstijging, getijverandering en Deltaveiligheid.* Report DGW-92. (Draft). October. Netherlands: DGW

EUROflood Project (1992) *Inception Report.* London, UK: Middlesex University

Hoozemans, F.M.J. (1989) Analyse van windgegevens van lichtschepen voor de Nederlandse kust. Nota GWAO 89.010. Netherlands: Rijkswaterstaat, Dienst Getijdewateren

Huybrechts, P. and Oerlemans, J. (1990) Response of the Antarctic ice sheet to future greenhouse warming. *Climate Dynamics* 5, 93–102

IPCC (1990) *Climate Change. Scientific Assessment.* Report prepared for the IPCC by Working Group 1 (Houghton, J.T.; Jenkins, G.J. and Ephraums, J.J., eds)

IPCC (1992a) *Climate Change 1992.* Supplementary Report to the IPCC Scientific Assessment. Report prepared for the IPCC by Working Group 1 (Houghton, J.T.; Callander, B.A. and Varney, S.K.)

IPCC (1992b) *Preliminary Guidelines for Assessing Impacts of Climate Change.* Working Group 2 of the IPCC

IUCC (1993) *Climate Change Dossier.* Chatelaine, Switzerland: United Nations Environment Programme (UNEP)

Kwadijk, J.C.J. (1991) Sensitivity of the River Rhine Discharge to Environmental Change: a first tentative assessment. *Earth Surface Processes and Landforms,* 16, 627–37

Kwadijk, J.C.J. and Middelkoop, H. (1992) Estimation of the Impact of Climate Change on the Peak Discharge Probability of the River Rhine. Submitted to *Climate Change*

Labrijn, A. (1945) Het klimaat van Nederland gedurende de laatste twee en een halve eeuw. *Mededelingen en Verhandelingen van het KNMI,* 49

Langendoen, E.J. (1987) *Onderzoek naar de vergroting van het getijverschil te Vlissingen.* Report no. 5-87. Delft, Netherlands: Technical University

Ministry of Housing, Physical Planning and the Environment (1991) *Onze kennis over klimaatverandering, verslag van een workshop.* Report no. Lucht 99. Netherlands: Ministry of Housing, Physical Planning and the Environment

Ministry of Housing, Physical Planning and the Environment (1992) *The Netherlands' Memorandum on Climate Change: Executive Summary.* CCD/Paper 4, April 1992. Netherlands: Ministry of Housing, Physical Planning and the Environment

Ministry of Public Health, Physical Planning and Environment (1992) *CHANGE* (Research and policy newsletter on global change from the Netherlands), 11 October. Netherlands: Ministry of Public Health, Physical Planning and Environment

Oerlemans, J. (1993) Factors Contributing to Sea Level Rise on a Decade to Century Time Scale. For: Sea Level Changes and their Consequences for Hydrology and Water Management. Noordwijkerhout, Netherlands, 19–23 April

Oerlemans, J. and Fortuin, J.P.F. (1992) Sensitivity of Glaciers and Small Ice Caps to Greenhouse Warming. *Science,* 258, 2 October

Ronde, J.G. de and Heinen, P.F. (1993) *Tide Gauge Records along the Dutch Coast.* The Hague, Netherlands: Ministry of Transport, Public Works and Water Management

Ronde, J.G. de and Vogel, J.A. (1988) *Technical Report 6* (TR6). Zeespiegelrijzing. Hydro Meteo scenario's. Note GWA0-88.015. February

Siegmund, P.C. (1990) *The Effect of Doubling of Atmospheric CO_2 on the Stormtracks in the Climate of a General Circulation Model.* Scientific report WR90-01. Royal Netherlands Meteorological Institute

Wigley, T.M.L. and Raper, S.C.B. (1992) Implications for Climate and Sea Level of Revised IPCC Emissions Scenarios. *Nature,* 357, 28 May

CHAPTER 3

Vulnerability Refined: Analysing Full Flood Impacts

Colin Green, Anne van der Veen, Erik Wierstra and
Edmund Penning-Rowsell

INTRODUCTION

As indicated in Chapter 1, we are concerned in flood hazard assessment and management with managing the interface between physical hazards and human systems: balancing the adoption of different counter-hazard strategies with the impacts of the flood events that would otherwise occur. This process involves choices, and to make those choices requires information.

Experience shows that systematic information on flood losses – and in particular those losses predicted to occur in the future – should 'drive' flood hazard assessment and management. Therefore, the main purpose of assessing the losses which would result from coastal erosion or flooding is to be an aid to reaching a decision as to what action to take. At its simplest, the decision may simply be to determine how severe the consequences of a series of flood events or a sea-level rise would be (Cline 1992, Nordhaus 1993). More generally, the decision is about what policy to adopt, or whether to take action in one particular location, and what plan or what programme of measures to adopt. Project appraisal methods are then decision aids to support such choices.

A project appraisal method has four components. First, there is a set of alternative options which are to be compared, where one is the baseline option: usually the 'do nothing' option. Secondly, some set of objectives are defined against which the performance of the different options, including the 'do nothing' option, are to be compared together with constraints which limit the possible options which may be considered. Thirdly, we need a set of ethical principles by which to compare the consequences of the different options where these may differ widely in terms of who is affected, what is the effect and when this effect occurs. Some common yardstick or numeraire is required with which to compare the different consequences. Finally, a rigorous framework of analysis is required whereby we can compare the different options against the objectives.

For public investments, the objectives to be adopted are socially determined and so too must be the ethical principles necessary to enable the comparison of options whose consequences are different and differently distributed over time and individuals. The objectives to be considered include economic efficiency, to which objective benefit-cost analysis is normally limited. But other objectives such as the equitable distribution of income or environmental enhancement might also be chosen.

Constraints may also be set which limit whether an option may be selected, however well it may perform against the objectives. Increasingly, the concept of sustainable development is being applied as a constraint which limits the choice of the option to be adopted rather than as an objective to be maximised. If an option fails to satisfy some criterion of sustainable development (Pearce and Warford 1993) then it must be rejected irrespective of its performance against the objective.

That the options differ in their distributions of the consequences results in ethical or value judgements being required to compare them. It may, for example, be necessary to balance a reduction in the risk of loss of life against some environmental damage. Project appraisal methods are therefore not and cannot be value free.

Project appraisal methods: overview
A variety of project appraisal methods is available, including benefit-cost analysis, environmental assessment and multi-criteria analysis.

Possible criteria for the selection of a project appraisal method include, first, that it clarifies the basic issues at stake in the decision – it is essential that the appraisal leaves the decision makers better informed about the nature of the decision than they would otherwise be. Secondly, the method should simplify the complexity of the choice to a manageable level. It should also incorporate the objectives and ethical principles considered to be appropriate to the choice, and it should include all of the important consequences of the different options as these relate to the specified objectives. Finally, the method should provide a rigorous and reliable framework for analysis and comparison.

Against these criteria, no single project appraisal method is always the best choice. Often a combination of methods will be required.

Nor can any appraisal method result in a better decision than the options being considered. It can only indicate which is the 'best' option of those available to be considered. Therefore, great care must be given to the search for possible options. It is highly desirable that decision processes be appraisal led; that the possible advantages and disadvantages of taking some action other than 'do nothing' are assessed before becoming committed to a single or narrow range of options. One rule for determining the options to be considered is that given by the US Water Resources Council (1983) which indicates that the project appraisal should take into account all national, environmental and regional considerations; little guidance is offered, however, as to what to do when these conflict, as they often do.

In addition, it is essential in the case of coastal erosion protection schemes, in particular, to consider when to undertake a scheme, if at all. It may sometimes be better to wait, allowing low value land and property to be lost, and undertake protection works for high value property only when these are immediately threatened by erosion. Again, in the face of sea-level rise, choosing the locations to protect is an important option. Both managed retreat – retiring the defence line behind the existing coastline and allowing some land to be lost – and selective protection in the form of strong points are options which should be considered. In the case of flood alleviation, one component of the choice should be the design standard of protection.

Two well-known project appraisal methods are benefit-cost analysis (BCA) and multi-criteria analysis (MCA). Of these methods, the objectives and ethical assumptions are only explicit in BCA. In MCA these value judgements are left to the decision maker employing the analysis. As grounded in neo-classical economics, BCA sets the objective as the maximisation of economic efficiency as measured by the criterion of the Hicks-Kaldor Compensation Principle. The two most important ethical assumptions embodied in neo-classical economic analysis are, first, that the value of a resource or good is solely assigned by individuals based on their own preferences; value is thus instrumental and a measure of the good's contribution to the individual's ends. Secondly, the assumption is made that individuals act rationally and maximise their self-interest however each individual defines his/her self-interest.

It is important to note the narrow definition of 'value' embodied in these axioms: other concepts or components of value such as the possible inherent value of a species by right of existence (Naess 1993) are excluded. More problematically, some, but only some, neo-classical economists have arbitrarily narrowed the definition of self-interest to selfishness, thereby excluding such motivations as altruism and duty from the ambit of neo-classical economics. In so far as such motives do underlie individual and social choices, an analysis restricted to narrow self-interest will yield misleading conclusions.

Whilst limiting itself to individually given values, economic analysis distinguishes between two forms of instrumental value: use and non-use value. The first is consumptive use: the value gained by consuming or making use of the good. The non-use value of a resource results from the other motives or reasons why the individual values that resource. Values in these terms are typically considered to depend upon the continued existence of the resource rather than its consumption (Pearce and Turner 1990). There is some evidence that altruistic motivations or ethical or moral beliefs (Green and Tunstall 1993) underlie non-use values.

To enable the comparison of different consequences, economics uses money as a yardstick or numeraire. Although using money as the numeraire, BCA is not limited to the evaluation of goods which have a market price. Indeed, it is usually necessary to make some correction to market prices – to use shadow prices – if the opportunity cost of the resource is to be correctly estimated. Where a good is not marketed, other techniques such as the Contingent Valuation Method (Mitchell and Carson 1989) and Conjoint Analysis (Louviere 1988) can be used to estimate the opportunity cost of the resource.

BCA does not address the question of the distribution of benefits and costs between different parties, and considers only the sum of resources. The varying distribution of benefits and costs over time is handled by the technique of discounting (Lind 1982). This is justified on two grounds: individual time preferences and the opportunity cost of capital. Unfortunately, the former argument does not lead necessarily to the conventional form of discounting (Newsome and Green 1993). Similarly, there are some concerns as to the use of a single discount rate (Krutilla and Fisher 1975) for streams of benefits and costs which differ widely in their characteristics (see Chapter 5). It is therefore desirable to plot the trajectories of the different streams of benefits and costs over time for the different options in addition to discounting in the conventional way (Penning-Rowsell *et al.* 1992a).

Thus, BCA is a mono-objective appraisal method which is based upon a restricted definition of value and one where there would be difficulty in extending it to cover a wider range of values using money as a yardstick. Whilst it possesses the rigour which Environmental Assessment lacks, it is often necessary to use it in combination with Environmental Assessment (Walthern 1988) or Environmental Mediation (Boer *et al.* 1991).

MCA (Nijkamp and Van Delft 1977, Nijkamp *et al.* 1990) was developed in response to the perceived narrow range of objectives and values which BCA could handle. As the name implies, the decision maker can choose any set of objectives against which to compare the options available. An efficient option is then one for which no alternative option performs at least as well against all the criteria. To choose amongst the efficient options, a decision rule must be developed which is some weighted measure of the performance of an option against each criterion. It is up to the decision maker, therefore, to decide what weights should be adopted and also to consider how to weight the distribution of consequences over time.

Therefore, the primary advantage of MCA is its flexibility: it is a helpful way of exploring the performance of the available options against whatever objectives are deemed to be appropriate. Moreover, it can allow the decision maker to explore what weights to give to the different objectives. Against these advantages, it has a number of off-setting disadvantages. Whilst it enables the selection of the 'best' of the options considered, it does not enable an assessment to be made as to whether any of the options is worthwhile. The resources required to undertake the best option might instead be used to provide education or health care, for example. Thus, whilst it is a useful method of internal comparison, it is weak in regard to external comparisons. Conversely, BCA is centred around external comparison. Again, whilst the value judgements associated with the objectives selected and the weights chosen are made explicit, it may be debatable whether these are shared by anyone other than the individual or group undertaking the MCA. For this reason, MCA in the form of

Multi-attribute Utility Analysis (Keeney and Raiffa 1976) is often used in the form for facilitating conflict resolution between groups viewed as having a stake in the decision (Winterfeldt and Edwards 1986).

THE BENEFITS OF COUNTER-FLOOD MEASURES: APPROACHES AND PRACTICES

Governments and other agencies – such as insurance and reinsurance companies – have sought to estimate either the benefits of coastal protection or flood alleviation schemes, or, alternatively, the likely losses from the flooding or sea-level rise. An important distinction must be made between the economic losses and the financial losses from such an event. Although insurance companies are always concerned with the financial consequences, governments vary in their interest. Where the government either compensates victims for their losses or acts as the insurer of the last resort, then the government will be concerned with the financial impacts as well as the economic loss to the national economy.

Coast protection delays erosion, thereby delaying the loss of the productive value of the land and its fixed assets or the inherent value of that resource. Flood alleviation reduces the risk of land being flooded where such a flood may damage the assets and the land itself, thereby reducing the productive capacity of those resources for some period of time whilst repairs are undertaken and replacements made. Erosion results in an irreparable loss of the assets concerned, whereas flooding generally causes damage which may be repaired.

The benefits of a flood alleviation or coast protection scheme – and by 'scheme' here we mean any counter-flood measure – are consequently the losses which are avoided by the scheme when compared to the 'do nothing' option. Methods for assessing the benefits of flood alleviation and coast protection schemes have developed in a number of countries (Greenaway and Smith 1983, Higgins 1981, Penning-Rowsell and Chatterton 1977, River Planning Division 1990).

Flooding may also cause health damage and other losses to inhabitants. Loss of non-priced assets such as treasured letters and photographs has been shown to be one of the worst effects of floods for those who have been flooded (Parker *et al.* 1987). Similarly, the stress of the flood itself may be considerable (Gleser *et al.* 1981, Green 1988, Miller *et al.* 1981, Powell and Penick 1983), and this can result in long-term health damage to those who have experienced a flood (Allee *et al.* 1980), as well as increasing their worry and anxiety about flooding in the future. In extreme floods, lives may be lost.

People may also have to leave their homes either as a precautionary measure when a flood warning is given or because their homes are uninhabitable after the flood. Evacuation, particularly where family or social structures are disrupted (Chamberlaine *et al.* 1981), has been found to be particularly distressing. In any event, the process of cleaning, repairing and replacing lost possessions is both long drawn out and itself a cause of stress.

The extent of the damages caused by a flood have been found to depend upon the depth of flooding, the duration of flooding, the velocity of water flow, the quantity of debris carried by the water and the silt load deposited, and any contaminants carried by the water. Salt water results in more damage than riverine water but contamination with sewage is common in river flooding. Generally, sewerage flooding is regarded by those who experience it with particular revulsion, not least because of the smell.

Methods of assessing the reduction in flood losses which a project will yield have been developed in France (Torterotot 1988), Germany (Merkblatter zur Wasserwirtschaft 1989) and the United Kingdom (Penning-Rowsell and Chatterton 1977) as well as in countries outside Europe (Greenaway and Smith 1983, River Planning Division 1990).

The principal determinant of damages is the depth of flooding, itself the difference between the flood level and the floor level of the property. This normally imposes a major data constraint on assessments of flood damages and the benefits of flood alleviation. Unless flooding is expected to be in excess of 2 m in depth, then it is necessary to be able to estimate reasonably accurately the floor levels of the properties at risk. Above about 2 m depth of flooding, the depth-damage curves tend to saturate and errors in estimates of the depths of flooding are relatively unimportant. But for lesser depths, errors in the estimation of the depth of flooding in the individual property of less than ± 5 cm are desirable.

Moreover, for two reasons, the shallower the flooding, the more critical is the estimate of floor levels of the affected buildings. First, the error in the estimate of the losses from a particular flood will be significant. Secondly, the most frequent floods are shallow floods and it is the losses from the frequent floods which contribute most to the estimation of the benefits of flood alleviation. The required accuracy limits the extent to which aerial mapping and geographic information systems (GIS) can currently be relied upon.

Losses can be measured either by the change in the stock of assets as these are destroyed or by the change in flows which those assets yielded. The value of land, for example, is the capitalised value of the productive use of that land. Since stock and flow changes are measures of the same thing it is consequently incorrect to count both. However, it is sometimes more convenient to measure a particular type of loss in terms of the change in stock and another type of loss by the change in flow.

An exception is when a stock loss results in a flow loss: the destruction of a machine tool may result in a loss of production while the machine tool is being replaced. Simply taking the loss as the capital value of the machine tool ignores the loss of production during the delay; the direct loss results in an additional indirect loss. Similarly, if flooding disrupts the electricity system then the disruption to production in factories which are not flooded but lack power is an indirect loss.

Direct damages

Extensive work has been undertaken in several different countries on the damages caused to buildings and their contents by flooding (BCEOM 1990, Buck 1988, Grigg and Helweg 1975, Günther 1987, Günther and Schmidtke 1988, Higgins 1981, Homan and Waybur 1960, Penning-Rowsell and Chatterton 1977, River Planning Division 1990). This work has shown that the depth of flooding is generally the most critical variable for urban flooding. In the development of standard data sets for predicting likely flood damages, two basic approaches have developed: areal depth-damage curves (Penning-Rowsell and Chatterton 1977) and unit loss approaches (Debo and Day 1980).

The former approach generates a curve which predicts the monetary value of the loss if a particular class of building is flooded to a particular depth and expresses this loss either per property or per unit area of such property. The unit loss approach expresses the loss as a proportion of the value at risk (see Chapter 4).

Probably the main determinant of the approach adopted is the prior availability of data on the values of buildings and contents at risk between countries. In those countries where a reliable, publicly available database exists, perhaps as part of the taxation system, unit loss approaches have commonly been adopted (Debo and Day 1980, River Planning Division 1990). Where such a database is not available, then areal depth-damage curves have been developed (Greenaway and Smith 1983, Penning-Rowsell and Chatterton 1977).

The two approaches have different advantages and disadvantages in application and development. The areal depth-damage approach requires surveys from maps with some ground-truthing to determine what properties are at risk. Using a GIS should reduce the work required but the availability of data on this reduction is as yet limited. Given that the depth of flooding is typically the critical determinant of damages, where the depth of flooding is the difference between the property floor level and the flood level, site surveys are typically required in order to estimate floor levels.

The great disadvantage of unit loss approaches is that the tax database is unlikely to yield information on the vertical distribution of property and contents. Where some properties are multi-storey, much of the reported value of the building and contents will be well above any conceivable depth of flooding. Separating out the value at risk from the total value can be difficult. Equally, the tax data may be of limited reliability or accuracy, not least because they are prepared for entirely different purposes.

Studies of damage data collected in different developed countries (Higgins and Robinson 1980, Green 1993) have shown that when depth-damage data are presented in the form of unit loss curves then the shape and location of the curve is similar between data sets for different countries. This means that it is reasonable to apply the unit loss curve derived from one country to another country in the absence of any local data. Two restrictions apply however. First, this is most true for the damage curves for residential data; there is much less similarity between the curves for non-residential data. Secondly, it is true only over relative shallow depths of flooding – up to, say, 1.2 m.

These two restrictions probably reflect weaknesses in the availability of data: variance within apparently similar types of industrial and commercial properties is so great that very much larger sample sizes would be required before the exact form of the depth-damage curve could be established precisely. Similarly, the best data are available for relatively shallow depths of flooding: there are no very good data on losses for, say, 3 m of flooding simply because it does not happen very often.

The damage data themselves can be prepared in one of two ways: survey data or synthetic data. Comparison between the results of the two approaches suggests that they give broadly similar results (Green 1993, Higgins and Robinson 1980).

The damages which a particular property experienced in a flood can be ascertained by a survey or the property owner can be asked what damages would be expected to result from a future flood. Similarly, specialised assessors, such as insurance loss adjusters, can be used to estimate the losses which would be expected in a particular property from a flood of a given magnitude. This approach is typically quite expensive in terms of the cost per property surveyed and when the overall sample size required is taken into account. Given the variation in the damageability of apparently quite similar types of property and the variety of different types of construction and use, a large sample size is required if the results are to be reliable.

Care must be taken to ensure that economic values rather than financial values are derived. Loss adjusters, for example, may allow for the 'insurance claim' effect whereby contractors charge higher prices when the costs will be reimbursed through insurance. Equally, the reliability and accuracy of surveys, particularly by inexperienced assessors, may be questionable.

A 'synthetic' approach involves using expert assessors to assess the losses which would be experienced from a 'typical' property type. Probably the best-known example of this approach is that adopted by Penning-Rowsell and Chatterton (1977), where building surveyors were employed to assess the damages which would be expected to a series of different standard house types. Market research data were then used to estimate what furniture and fittings each such house would contain and specialist assessors were used to estimate the proportional loss to each such item. The major difficulty in this approach is ensuring that the standard property types are truly representative of actual properties and that all important categories of contents are included.

In applying damage data derived by either approach to assess the flood damages which could be expected from a specific flood, a key component is some system of land use classification. This identifies what buildings are to be regarded as being of equivalent damage-ability. The ideal system would cluster buildings in terms of known equivalent damageability and would also be easy to use. In practice, the latter criterion has guided the development of land use classification systems. Apartments, for example, may be distinguished from detached houses, and butcher's shops are distinguished from bakeries.

On the industrial and commercial side, the typical practice is to base the classification system on some existing classification system used for other purposes. In France, for example, the MOS classification system is that used in a GIS of land uses (SIEE 1993). Similarly, in the United Kingdom the classification used is derived from the system used in the preparation of government industrial statistics. Such practices make the classification systems easy to apply. Where a unit loss approach is adopted then it is essential that the land use classification system is compatible with that used in the asset database. However, in the ideal classification system, variance in damageability of properties within the same class would be minimised whilst the variance between classes would be maximised. The evidence is, however, that variance is often very considerable within a class of industrial or commercial properties (Parker *et al.* 1987) and there is no evidence that existing classification systems are efficient in clustering properties which have similar flood damageability.

Indirect losses
Indirect or consequential flood losses result from either the direct damages caused by the flood or the existence of the flood itself. Therefore, the two critical determinants of the magnitude of indirect financial losses are the extent of the direct damages and the duration of the resulting disruption. Consequently, the duration of the flood is important as the loss of production during a flood lasting 10–15 days can be significant. In extreme events, indirect losses may exceed direct damages.

When economic losses are considered, then a third factor must be added: the extent to which the losses can be made up elsewhere in the economy. It may, for example, be possible for other factories to make up the production lost by those flooded. For this reason, there can be a very significant difference between the financial and economic indirect losses from a flood. For shops, for example, it would normally be expected that there would be no economic losses although the financial impacts to the shops affected might be catastrophic in the absence of consequential loss insurance.

Evaluating the flood-induced disruption of road traffic is relatively easy to undertake since most countries undertake BCA of major new roads (Hargest *et al.* 1991). The same data and models necessary to evaluate such proposals can be applied to the evaluation of the disruption caused by flooding (Parker *et al.* 1987).

Another component of indirect costs is the costs incurred in trying to minimise the losses which would otherwise result from a flood. These costs include the costs of the emergency services and of emergency works. Any counselling provided to victims is also justified in these terms, as are the medical costs of treatment. Again, the costs of additional heating and dehumidifiers to dry out affected properties are a relevant cost.

The costs of temporary rehousing for those who have to leave their homes is significant in some instances; the relevant economic cost here is that of providing an equivalent standard of accommodation to their own home.

Scheme negative benefits
Whilst projects are intended to protect property and often areas of environmental value from damage or loss, the projects themselves may have negative effects; these need to be counted too.

Thus, in the case of engineering works, the process of scheme construction often results in noise and dirt, and in disruption to those living nearby. The form of the scheme may result in a loss of amenity to local residents whose view of the sea or river is impaired. There may also be environmental damages; indeed, in coastal areas it is often impossible to find any option, including the 'do nothing' option, which is free of environmental dis-benefits. Finally, reducing coastal erosion in one area will have effects on other areas downdrift, either through the 'last groyne' effect or by reducing the supply of sediment or both. The consequence of reducing erosion in one place may be increased erosion in another; this latter loss must be counted with the dis-benefits of the first scheme. It is therefore necessary to identify and evaluate where possible all of these negative effects, particularly the opportunity cost of the reduction in the sediment supply.

CONCEPTUAL MODELLING: UNPACKING THE NATURE OF FLOOD VULNERABILITY

This chapter so far has shown the need for adequate quantification of flood hazard impacts to aid decision making and choices about options to alleviate that hazard. This, then, is the point of departure of our research, which starts from the base position of needing to know more about the vulnerability of European populations to flood hazards, and about the shifts in this vulnerability that climate change might induce. We therefore start by exploring definitions of vulnerability, 'unpacking' that concept to reveal its contributory elements, and thereby developing a comprehensive conceptual model of vulnerability to flooding.

We know at the outset that vulnerability to flood hazards is created by a combination of many variables, including those concerned with human activities and those concerned with the physical nature of the location of those activities; the latter includes the nature of the fluvial or coastal flood event itself. Some of these have been reviewed already in this chapter, but now we want to take this further.

Therefore we need to recognise that vulnerability can increase both as floods increase in frequency or severity, and also as populations become less capable of coping with or adapting to the floods that have an impact on their activities; this kind of idea is central to Figure 1.1 in Chapter 1. This lack of adapting behaviour can be owing to a false perception of the exposure to risk or an inability to respond to floods when they occur, or a combination of both.

Thus vulnerability must be seen as a function both of the physical systems that lead to the physical conditions that we term floods, and of the human systems that are affected (Penning-Rowsell *et al.* 1986). Therefore our first definition of vulnerability has a general form and is represented in a very general way in both Equation 1 and Figure 1.1:

Vulnerability = f [physical characteristics + human characteristics]

(Equation 1)

However we know that this is a gross oversimplification, and part of our research is aimed at calibrating the above equation by expanding on it and researching its elements. This means that its constituent parts need to be broken down and analysed. That has been done for a limited number of parts of Europe, mainly the United Kingdom and France (Parker *et al.* 1987, Torterotot and Roche 1990) and for certain types of flood events (mainly slow rise fluvial floods and certain types of coastal events), and the gaps in knowledge here will be filled as our research progresses.

First, we can break the above equation down by examining the main factors which constitute and affect vulnerability, in this case taking the vulnerability of people in domestic household situations first because this is the area where most research has been undertaken in the past.

Expanding on Equation 1 we get Equation 2 below, which includes an element of the character of the flood itself (the flood characteristics), and also both the human characteristics of those in the flood prone area and the nature of the response to those flooded by society at large:

Household vulnerability = f [socio-economic characteristics], [property and infrastructure characteristics], [flood characteristics], [warning characteristics], [response characteristics]

(Equation 2)

It should not be taken that the significance of the blocks of characteristics are equal in any way, and therefore that the flood's characteristics are dominated by the other characteristics. Indeed, the flood characteristics could themselves no doubt be broken down further into a number of categories of characteristics, but that is not the main objective of our research as it is more properly the domain of the hydrologist, the hydrographer and the flood engineer (Saul 1992).

Again Equation 2 is clearly a simplification, and we need to break down the parts of each of the blocks of characteristics so that quantification and calibration becomes possible. This is done in Equation 3 (shown in Figure 3.1) and, of course, each variable listed there is in reality a summary surrogate for many different aspects of the factors that contribute to household vulnerability, each of which is discussed below in turn.

Many of the points made in this section, then, are still hypotheses and intuitive judgements based on experience of many floods and their impacts. However, in a later section of this chapter we report on further research which had begun more rigorously to calibrate the equation, based on a large number of surveys of householders who had experienced flooding. We separate these two sections in this chapter in order to give, first, the comprehensive set of ideas and hypotheses in the form of the model presented in Figure 3.1, followed by, secondly, the more restricted calibration results.

	Social/economic variables	Property and infrastructure variables	Flood characteristics	Warning variables	Response variables

$$\text{Household Vulnerability} = f\left[\frac{A,}{H,S,I,C,F}\right], \left[\frac{S_c,S_b,I_t}{S_t,R_o}\right], \left[D_e,D_t,S_d,S_t,W,V,P_l,R\right], \left[\overline{W_o,W_t,W_a}\right], \left[\overline{T_r,R_a,R_q}\right]$$

O = Low density
1 = High density
A = Age profile of household
H = Health status and/or mobility of household
S = Savings of household
I = Income of household
C = Cohesiveness of local community
F = Flood knowledge

S_c = Susceptibility of building contents to damage
S_b = Susceptibility of building fabric
I_r = Time taken to restore infrastructure (especially sewerage, electricity and telecommunications)
S_t = Number of storeys
R_o = Robustness of building fabric (density)

D_e = Depth of flooding
D_t = Duration of flooding
S_d = Sediment concentration
S_t = Sediment size
W = Wave/wind action (i.e. coastal or not)
V = Velocity
P_l = Pollution load of flood waters
R = Rate of water rise during flooding onset

W_o = Warning given or not
W_t = Warning time provided
W_a = Advice content of warning

T_r = Time taken for assistance to arrive after or during event
R_a = Amount of response (number of people assisting)
R_q = Response quality

Figure 3.1: The definition of flood hazard vulnerability as applied to households.

Social/economic variables (variables *A, H, S, I, C* and *F*)

Other things being equal, the research evidence so far has suggested that elderly populations, or elderly individuals within populations, are more vulnerable to floods than the young, especially if the flood event arrives suddenly with little warning (Green *et al.* 1985). The elderly are less able to respond with flood fighting actions, and are more likely to be infirm so that response is slower and less effective (Parker *et al.* 1983). Those with most knowledge are less vulnerable.

In the same way those with higher health status (i.e. those less unwell) are more able to respond to floods, and those households that have a large family (or family members in the immediate vicinity) are less vulnerable because help can arrive quickly and households can respond to the hazard that they face (Green and Penning-Rowsell 1986). A strongly cohesive local community will probably have the same or a similar effect by being able to assist in reducing the impacts of floods, whereas a community where there is little intergroup contact will be less likely to be able to cope (Green *et al.* 1985).

There is at least some evidence (Green and Penning-Rowsell 1989) that those households with higher incomes or more ready access to savings can help themselves more readily in flood events and are therefore less vulnerable to their impacts. Much of the continuing impact of floods after the flood waters have subsided is in the aggravation caused in the protracted negotiations with insurance companies and their agents, and those flood victims who have their own financial resources immediately available to cope with extreme events will be able to cope with this negotiation more easily and with less impact (Green and Penning-Rowsell 1989).

Thus, in summary, households composed of young people with financial reserves are less vulnerable to floods than those of the elderly, the poor and the sick. This is probably true for other hazards. There may be intervening variables and different variables for different flood types, and this needs further investigation.

Property and infrastructure variables (variables *Sc, Sb, It, St* and *Ro*)

If buildings have more than one storey, their contents may be moved to safety upon receipt of flood warnings and damage will consequently be lower than if the buildings are just one storey high. The damage will also be lower if the buildings are robustly built, for example from stone or brick rather than timber and plasterwork (Penning-Rowsell and Chatterton 1977).

The susceptibility of household contents and building fabric to damage will depend on their type and age, but in general soft furnishings are more susceptible to damage than wooden furniture, and electrical goods – especially electronic goods – are usually a total damage item when affected by severe and prolonged flooding.

The time that is needed to restore services to a dwelling also affects the damage caused (Parker *et al.* 1987). This is because without electricity the drying of flooded goods is difficult, and while sewerage systems are not functioning the dwelling becomes virtually un-inhabitable and therefore damage is greater than would otherwise be the case. Obviously telecommunications connections mean that assistance can be organised more quickly and easily, including in the clean-up and repair phase of the restoration of the building to normality (Parker *et al.* 1987).

The impact of the flood's characteristics (variables *De, Dt, Sd, St, W, Pl, R* and *V*)

Floods vary considerably in their characteristics and therefore their impact and damage.

Generally, the deeper the flood and the higher the flood water velocity the greater will be the damage, which will also be exacerbated by high speed of onset and long flood duration (Penning-Rowsell and Chatterton 1977, Torterotot and Roche 1990). In some cases duration of flooding is more important than depth, especially if this duration has major secondary impacts on economic systems and communities (Parker *et al.* 1987). If flooding at the coast leaves property exposed to the effects of waves during storm events, then this will cause considerable extra damage including the risk of structural failure of the building (Penning-Rowsell *et al.* 1992a).

The character of the flood waters will also affect the damage caused, and therefore the impact of the flood. Pollution in flood water can have serious long-term impacts, including effects on the health of the people affected. Almost all floods in urban areas will be contaminated with sewage, which increases clean-up costs and causes distress and the possibility of disease (Green and Tunstall 1991).

In certain areas, and particularly where flood water velocities are high, high sediment concentrations in flood waters will also heighten damage caused and therefore increase the vulnerability of households affected by these circumstances. The larger the sediment size and the greater the velocity of flood waters, the greater the likelihood of boulders and other material damaging buildings and harming their occupants. Finally, the higher the rate of rise of the flood waters, the less warning that can be given – other things being equal – and therefore the more vulnerable will be the populations at risk (Torterotot and Roche 1990).

Warning variables (variables *Wo*, *Wt* and *Wa*)

Warnings can reduce both the tangible and the intangible damage caused by floods (Parker 1991), and the availability and value of warnings can therefore influence vulnerability. As indicated above, the rate of rise or onset of flooding will determine to some extent whether a warning can be made and issued, and the length of warning time will influence what can be done between the warning being received and the flood occurring (Parker and Tunstall 1991, Torterotot and Roche 1990).

Much research has been done on the many variables affecting the quality of the warning, both in terms of lead time and the process of warning dissemination, and the type of message sent. In general it appears that the greater the advice content of the warning, the greater its effectiveness and therefore the lower the vulnerability of the population being warned (Handmer and Penning-Rowsell 1990).

However this is a complex matter and the quality of both the forecast of a flood and the warning as to what response to take is affected by a large number of variables that will help to determine aggregate vulnerability.

Response variables (variables *Tr*, *Ra* and *Rq*)

Warning and response are interconnected, as indeed are all the variables discussed above. Therein, again, lies the research challenge.

The time taken for assistance to arrive will affect the vulnerability of the most vulnerable in the flood-affected community. Swift response can save lives and reduce the health impacts of the flood on its victims, as well as helping to save damage (especially to heritage values in that art treasures may be saved from total damage if they are quickly removed from the flood waters).

In addition, the amount of response (the number of assistants, the number of police, the number of military personnel etc.) will affect the degree of response, if not the quality. There are of course countervailing factors: too many observers of the flood will not help the flood victims, although greater media attention to a flood event may mean that the media's audience can respond in other ways, perhaps by donating financial relief to those affected. This is an area where little is known about the effect of response types and amounts on vulnerability, and it deserves further research.

Finally, the quality of long-term response systems will affect the way in which the community returns to a normal state of affairs. It is known that trained social workers can assist in this process (Parker and Handmer 1992), and that even the attentions of interviewers from research organisations coming to interview flood victims many months after the event can have beneficial therapeutic effects for victims who angrily feel that the official sources of assistance have passed them by (Tunstall and Bossman-Aggrey 1988).

Household vulnerability assessment: calibration needs
Equation 3 (Figure 3.1) is complex, and has been semi-empirically and inductively derived from a small number of what are probably untypical flood event cases when taken in the Europe-wide context.

We thus, for example, know too little about the vulnerability of populations to flooding from the sea and from high intensity storms in southern Europe, and to situations where floods are accompanied by extreme cold.

The equation therefore needs further research to enhance our understanding and its calibration. When that enhancement is achieved, then it will be possible more clearly to identify, map and quantify the nature of household vulnerability to flooding in the European Union countries, and predict where vulnerability is likely to grow with climate change. This will undoubtedly assist in developing a more targeted and standardised policy response.

Defining the vulnerability of other human activities and assets
If progress is still needed on defining the variables and in calibrating the equations defining the vulnerability of households to flooding, then even less is known about the vulnerability of industrial, commercial and infrastructure systems to flooding – although some pioneering work was completed in the 1980s (Parker et al. 1987).

That research concentrated on the indirect effects of floods, rather than direct damages. It created another formula, which defines the nature of the vulnerability framework of these human activities to disruption by flooding. The formula's simplest expression is as below:

$$V = f(D, T, S) \qquad\qquad \text{(Equation 4)}$$

Where:

V = vulnerability to flood disruption;

D = dependence, the degree to which an activity requires a particular good as an input to function normally;

T = transferability, the ability of an activity to respond to a disruptive threat by overcoming dependence either by deferring the activity in time, or by relocation, or by using substitutes;

S = susceptibility, the probability and extent to which the physical presence of flood water will affect inputs or outputs of an activity.

Seen like this, an industrial or commercial activity will be dependent on the continued supply of a good – such as electricity – if even a brief disruption of this supply disrupts the activity. Therefore a factory will be dependent on the supply of electricity for its economic activity if it cannot operate without that supply, which may be disrupted by flooding. The susceptibility of the electricity intake of the factory – its physical exposure to and probability of flood damage – will control the vulnerability there, and if this susceptibility can be reduced in any way then the factory's vulnerability will be reduced. However, and in parallel, if the production of that factory can be transferred to another branch plant or deferred in time (or a combination of both), then the total vulnerability of the business concerned will be lessened or even eliminated. Obviously there may be cost penalties through deferring or transferring production in this way, and the extent of these costs reduces the lessening of vulnerability.

This formula can be used widely in a number of sectors (Parker *et al.* 1987). The diffusion of impacts of flooding into local, regional and national economies is not well understood and this will be one focus of our continuing research.

A somewhat different approach needs to be adopted when assessing the impacts of flooding and erosion at the coast. This is because the impacts of hazards there may more readily result in activities being relocated to another part of the coast, or to coasts in different countries.

The clearest example of this phenomenon is the impact of hazards on recreational activities. Here the erosion of a beach, or the flooding of land now associated with recreational activities, will result in losses there of recreational facilities and associated human enjoyment. This may be recouped by the population affected moving to nearby beaches, which can perhaps provide the same level of recreational enjoyment, maybe at slightly higher costs in travelling terms. Or the people affected may choose to select non-beach recreational activities for their enjoyment, or coastal activities in a different country, rather than persisting with the degraded recreational experience at the hazard-affected site.

This research area has been explored recently in the United Kingdom and a monograph has been produced which summarises the impacts of coastal erosion and flooding on the wide range of human activities to be found at the coast (Penning-Rowsell *et al.* 1992b). There is much more research that needs to be done in this complex situation, and an important continuing dimension of our Europe-wide research will be to continue to refine our work in these fields.

IMPACTS AND NON-MONETARY LOSSES: RESULTS FROM SURVEYS OF DOMESTIC HOUSEHOLDS

Overview

Although assessments of the losses caused by flooding have con-centrated upon the priced losses, these losses are often not those which are regarded as most important by the flood victims. Other losses such as health damage, the disruption caused by flooding and the loss of irreplaceable items are often seen as more important (Table 3.1). There is also the question of the loss of lives during floods.

For floods are dangerous, and can pose a significant risk to life compared to many human-induced – 'non-natural' – hazards. Typically, however, the risk of death if a flood occurs is relatively low: usually less than 1 in 1,000. Thus, generally, although the risk of a flood is often high, the overall risk of death in an area at flood risk is low.

But the apparent relatively benign nature of flooding can be mis-leading. When either the flood velocity is high or the depth of water is

Table 3.1: Assessments by flood victims of the relative severity of different flood impacts.

	Mean	Standard deviation	Sample size (N)
Overall seriousness of effects	4.9	3.4	1580
Effects upon your family's health	5.2	3.2	590
Having to leave home	3.5	4.0	324
Damage to replaceable contents	5.9	3.3	306
Worry about flooding in the future	4.8	3.7	1587
Loss or damage of irreplaceable objects	6.4	3.5	293
Problems of getting the house back to normal	5.4	3.9	1391
Damage to the house itself	5.4.	3.3	377
Stress of the flood itself	5.0	3.8	1476
Effect on gardens, land and outbuildings	6.2	3.4	381
Foul smell of flood water	4.8	4.1	1171
Inconvenience caused by road flooding	4.4	3.8	740

scale: 0 'no effect'
10 'most serious effect'

great, the risk of death if a flood occurs is somewhat higher and may be in the region of 1 in 50. In such areas, the risk to life will often not satisfy the criteria of tolerable or acceptable risk normally applied to human-induced hazards such as nuclear power stations or chemical plants (Health and Safety Executive 1988).

In such areas, structural flood protection except to very high standards such as those adopted in the Netherlands (Chapter 5) will often not be sufficient to achieve standards of risk regarded as tolerable. Consequently, emergency plans covering warning and evacuation are essential in those areas.

Research priorities

For three reasons, work has been undertaken on quantifying these impacts and losses. First, we have sought to identify those combinations of event characteristics and populations for which such losses are most significant (see Figure 3.1). Secondly, we have wished to gauge the effectiveness of alternative intervention strategies to reduce some or all of these consequences. Finally, we have reviewed ways to include these losses into appraisals of flood alleviation schemes.

The reason for this research is that information in the literature is sparse and sometimes contradictory. The evidence of whether, for example, the elderly are more vulnerable to suffering health damage from floods is mixed (Huerta and Horton 1978, Poulshock and Cohen 1975, Price 1978). Similarly, it should be expected that a flood warning will reduce the stress experienced in a flood compared to that experienced in a flood which occurs without warning, but hitherto information on this important topic has been largely missing.

Additionally, there are other ideas and hypotheses to test. Post-disaster counselling (National Institute of Mental Health 1979) is increasingly commonplace and it is desirable to determine whether this is effective in reducing the long-term health damage to flood victims. Disasters also evoke spontaneous support from friends and relatives, and also community groups. In studies of UK flood victims, it has been found that the more severe the flood, the more likely it is that such spontaneous support is provided and the greater the value it is seen to have by the victims. However, the effectiveness and best form of such support has been an open question.

Surveys and results

A series of surveys has been undertaken emphasising household impacts and responses to floods. A number of measures for stress and worry have been developed (Tables 3.2 and 3.3). Existing survey instruments to measure distress, the longer-term consequence of stress, have also been used in interviews of flood victims (Table 3.4).

The full data set includes some 1,700 cases with some 500 variables, but not all the cases cover all of the variables. This data set, although large, is limited in the range of flood events covered. The floods included were predominantly of hours rather than days in duration and relatively shallow, generally less than 1.5 m in depth. This is important because it seems reasonable to expect that longer or deeper floods would cause relatively greater non-monetary impacts.

Another point to make is that the combinations of flood characteristics

Table 3.2: Event stress.

Statement	Proportion reporting %	Sample size (N)
I just wanted to run away	10	427
I knew I could cope	36	427
I didn't know what to do	15	427
I cried	11	427
I thought 'Oh no, not again'	32	427
I felt numb	11	427
I imagined that the worst was going to happen	19	427
It was a nightmare	47	427
I was very angry	35	427
I swore	24	427
I thought that I was going to have a heart attack	10	169
I felt sick	15	427
My pulse raced	15	427
I thought about what to do	35	427
I was horrified	22	427
I was excited	8	427
I thought that this was the worst possible time for it to happen	13	427
I knew what to do	10	427
I panicked	28	427
I felt hot and cold flushes	7	427
I was afraid that I was going to die	3	427
I called for help	0	427
I was terrified	15	427

and household characteristics represented in the sample data are not necessarily a representative sample of all the possible combinations that may occur. Therefore, the analysis was based on the conceptual model outlined earlier (Figure 3.1), and could only pick out the predominant linkages represented in the data set itself.

That model of vulnerability discriminates between the magnitude of the loss from the event and the subjective severity of a given

Table 3.3: Revealed worry (percentages agreeing with statements).

Statement	Percentage	Sample size (N)
We hardly worry about possible flooding	45	1167
If we go away, we arrange with neighbours how they can contact us in case of a flood	44	1323
We are so worried that we do not go on holiday or long visits	6	1133
When we go away on holiday or a visit, we move important things above possible floodwater levels	21	1235
We are afraid to go out when it rains heavily/there is a gale	17	1363
When it rains heavily/when river/tide levels are high, we move car to a safe area	15	1149
We are worried every time it rains heavily/river/tide levels are high	36	1366
We are afraid to go out when heavy rain/high river/high tide levels are forecast	15	1363
We stay up all night when storm forecast	11	1370
We would move to another house if we could	17	1361
When it rains, we check the water in the river/stream/sea	37	1202
We have stopped using the cellar	8	676
We have spent money to stop water entering house	22	1201
We are too worried to sleep at night when it rains heavily/when tide levels are high	19	1235
We keep a stock of candles, matches and supplies in case we are surrounded by a flood	50	1365
There is nothing we can do about flooding	71	116
We have given up trying with the garden	12	209

Table 3.4: Horowitz's impact of event scale.

Statement	Mean	Standard deviation	Sample size (N)
I thought about it when I didn't mean to	2.0	1.2	464
I avoided letting myself get upset when I thought or was reminded of the flood	1.9*	1.1	458
I tried to remove the flood from memory	1.9*	1.2	449
I had trouble falling asleep or staying asleep	1.6	1.0	453
I had waves of strong feelings about the flood	1.8	1.2	453
I had dreams about the flood	1.2	0.7	448
I feel as if it hadn't happened or that it wasn't real	1.4*	0.8	445
I tried not to talk about the flood	1.6*	1.0	452
Pictures about the flood popped into my mind	1.8	1.1	454
Other things kept making me think about the flood	1.7	1.0	449
I tried not to think about the flood	1.7*	1.1	448
Any reminder brought back feelings about the flood	1.9	1.1	451
My feelings about the flood were numbed	1.5*	1.0	444

* Avoidance scale

Scale: 1 'not at all'
       2 'rarely'
       3 'sometimes'
       4 'often'

magnitude of consequence. It is therefore a mediated model in that a given magnitude of loss can be mediated by intervening factors which either amplify or reduce the severity of the given magnitude of loss for a particular household. Similarly, mediating factors intervene between the characteristics of the flood and the magnitude of the loss experienced by a different combination of household and property.

If the critical characteristics of the flood itself are considered first, then it was found that the monetary value of the structural damage to properties was a function of the depth of flooding, when both the depth and the value of the loss were first transformed by a logarithmic function, but that detached houses suffered a significantly higher degree of structural damage for the same depth of flooding. For contents losses, again the financial value of the loss experienced by a property was a function of the depth of flooding, but this was mediated by whether or not the householder had received a flood warning prior to the onset of the event. Receipt of a flood warning resulted in a significantly lower level of loss to the house's contents.

However, the impacts of flooding were also significantly associated with characteristics of the flood event itself. Thus the stress experienced by the household was not only associated with the depth of flooding experienced in the area but significantly reduced if that flooding occurred during daylight hours. This particular association with daylight hours may simply be the result of the low number of people within the sample we analysed who had been warned. It may then indicate that knowledge of the imminence of a flood reduces stress.

Similarly, the length of time that a household takes to recover from a flood was a function not simply of the cost of the damage to the house but also of the depth of flooding in the local area. Of the whole sample, 29 per cent of householders left home either together or as individual members of the household for some period of time; we use the term 'left home' here rather than 'evacuation' to denote that this was a decision taken by the occupants and that the action was voluntary. One or more members of the household were more likely to leave home if the depth of flooding was greater. Also correlated with the propensity to leave home was the time of day of the flood: the later in the day the flood occurred the more likely it was that members of the household left their home. In addition, the loss of telephone contact was significant: if there was loss of telephone contact the householder was more likely to leave home, other things being equal. In addition, the infirm were more likely to leave home than the able residents.

As indicated above, there were a number of characteristics of the household which affected the overall severity or magnitude of the flood losses they experienced.

The mediating variables in which we were particularly interested were differences in the coping style of the individual household, the resources – financial and social – which they could mobilise to meet the challenge posed by a particular event, and different forms of social intervention.

In particular, this applied to various forms of social support, through not only friends and relatives but the more formal social support systems such as the social services and the emergency services. And again the effectiveness of flood warnings was important. These mediating variables might act either to reduce the magnitude of the loss or to moderate the severity of a given loss in terms of its resulting severity of impact on the household.

In terms of this overall model, then, the most critical variable identified was the stress induced by the event itself, as measured by the scale shown in Table 3.2. Not only was the stress induced by the event one of the most important consequences in subjective terms of all of those experienced, but it was important in determining, for example, whether or not a household reported suffering health effects.

Thus, whether or not a household reported experience of some health effect depended upon the degree of stress that they reported experiencing on the event/stress scale and on the degree of worry (Table 3.3) they felt about the possibility of future flooding. Some 38 per cent said their health had been affected and of these 21 per cent saw a doctor.

In turn the stress they experienced during the event was the primary determinant of whether or not they then sought medical advice about the health effect they perceived themselves as having experienced. The subjective severity of this health effect was then in turn determined by the severity of the stress they felt themselves to have experienced, whether or not they had sought medical advice. In addition, the elderly tended to report a higher degree of severity of health damage than did younger flood victims. The measure of event stress also proved to be a good predictor of the flood victims' reports of the severity of the stress that they had experienced.

It was noted earlier that the characteristics of the flood coupled with the infirmity of the occupants were the primary determinants of whether part or all of the household left their home during or after the flood. For the 29 per cent who did leave their home, the severity of this experience depended upon where they went and how much it cost them to do so. Interestingly, those who stayed with relatives were more likely to report a high level of severity for this impact than those who went elsewhere.

On average, then, the impact which was reported as having the greatest severity was the problem of getting the house back to normal again. This was not only affected by the duration of the disruption as measured in number of days, but the stress reported to have been received during the flood also entered into the assessment of the severity of this disruption.

The direct damages from the flood, as shown by Figure 3.2, did not directly impact on the overall severity of the flood experienced by the flood victims. Their importance was in determining the degree of disruption experienced by the members of that household.

Here the wealth of the family had a significant buffering effect on the severity of a given magnitude of loss. Those who reported their household as being more wealthy than the average family experienced a significantly lower severity of impact from a given value of contents loss than did poorer families. Similarly, for damages to the fabric of their home, those who either used up savings and/or reported financial problems as a result of the flood felt this loss to be greater than those who neither reported financial problems nor used up their savings. Therefore, the financial resources which individual households can mobilise form an important buffering element to impacts from a flood.

Other coping resources, using Lazarus's model (Lazarus 1966), were not found to have a significant buffering effect. We did not find that the style of coping in Folkman and Lazarus's (1980) terminology had any significant effect upon either the severity of stress or the health damage experienced. Nor was it possible to disentangle any effect of social support.

The results in respect of social support appear somewhat anomalous. Flood victims consistently rated the help they were given by friends, relatives and other sources as being very important. Yet those who received social support equally consistently reported more severe impacts from flooding. This was partly explained by the likelihood of social support being given to a flood victim depending upon the extremity of the flood they experienced. Social support was more likely to be offered if floods were deeper or lasted longer.

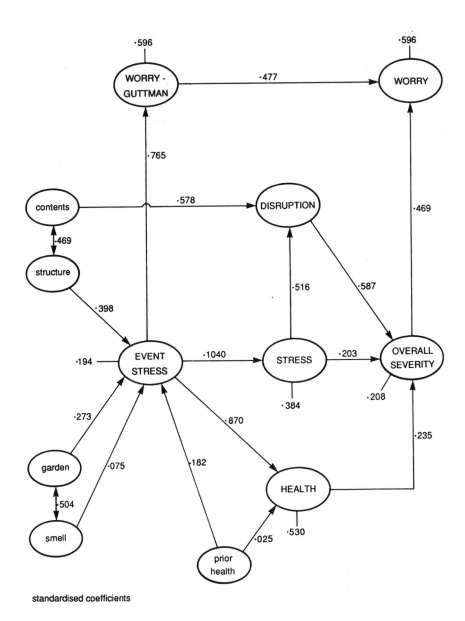

Figure 3.2: Causal model of relationships between impacts and judged overall severity of flooding.

However, even after taking account of the severity of the flood, it was not possible to identify any buffering effect of social support upon either the magnitudes of such consequences as disruption and health, nor upon the subjective severity of such impacts. In each case, the regression coefficients were typically in the right direction but were non-significant. Thus, the implication is that flood victims value the support they are offered by friends, relatives and others, yet this support has very little effect upon the final outcome for these flood victims.

This may suggest that the wrong sort of support is being offered or merely that the measures so far developed for social support are inadequate. Equally, the other form of intervention examined – flood warnings – was found to have a relatively small effect, where it could be identified. It was found that content losses were less in financial terms if the household had received a warning. It was also found, as indicated above, that the degree of stress householders experienced during a flood was less if that flood occurred in daylight hours.

The latter finding suggests that advance warning of potential flooding is potentially advantageous. The limitation in the analysis was that few of those who had actually received a flood warning had also completed the questionnaire which measures the stress of the event itself. Therefore, a tentative conclusion is that flood warnings are likely to reduce the stress experienced in a flood which, as described earlier, is one of the main determinants of the overall severity of the experience. This tentative conclusion is potentially supported by the finding that prior awareness of the flood risk tended to be associated with lower overall severity of impacts. Conversely, however, previous experience of flooding did not appear to buffer the overall severity of the consequences.

ASSESSMENT AND CONCLUSIONS

This chapter has reviewed the field of decision making and collated our best knowledge on the nature of flood vulnerability. It has also reported on the analysis of a large data set concerned with flooding to households, and this has given more insight into the nature of vulnerability and the effect of coping and intervention strategies.

We would like to emphasise a number of points by way of conclusions. These include our firm view that the development of flood alleviation and coastal zone protection projects and programmes should be 'appraisal led' rather than design led or politics led: appraisals should guide decisions rather than post-rationalising them. In this respect there is no single 'best' project appraisal method; all have various drawbacks and the best approach to adopt is a mixture of 'horses for courses' together with the use of two or more different approaches in any one instance.

Central to our thoughts in this respect should be the principle of sustainable development, and this is best embodied in our decision making as a constraint on the range of project alternatives which may be considered in a particular instance. With this in mind the initial selection of the engineering or policy options to be considered is critical to the final selection of the 'best' option. These options considered should include the environmentally best option, the 'do nothing' option and managed retreat (in the coastal zone situation), as well as different standards of protection and alternative dates of implementation.

As far as the data for appraising flood alleviation schemes are concerned, we continue to confirm that the direct damages from flooding are principally and most commonly dependent upon the depth and extent of flooding. The principal characteristic of flooding as this affects the magnitude of indirect losses is the duration of the flooding. Warnings are important to prevent damage, and also have beneficial impacts on the 'intangible' effects of floods on households. The non-monetary impacts of flooding on households are typically more important than the financial losses they experience.

This raises the question of data sets and their transferability within Europe. We believe that for depths of flooding of less than 1.5 m, depth-damage data in the form of unit loss data sets can be transferred from another country in the absence of any national data. However, the variance in damages between apparently similar non-residential properties is large. In developing standard damage data for residential properties, the best initial starting point is the 'synthetic' approach. These data should be validated at a latter date through obtaining site survey data.

But flood damage is not the only effect of floods. In some situations, the risk to life from flooding exceeds the risk normally deemed to be acceptable or tolerable. In these instances, typically in low-lying coastal zones, structural precautions need to be supplemented by warning and evacuation measures if a tolerable level of risk is to be achieved.

These conclusions have emerged partly from the research described in this volume and partly from many years of experience in analysing floods and flood alleviation schemes. It is notable in this respect that whilst there are differences that result from taking a European perspective, there are also similarities in both the data we have examined and the conclusions that can be reached.

REFERENCES

Allee, D.J.; Osgood, B.T.; Antle, L.G.; Simpkins, C.E.; Moltz, A.N.; Van der Slice, A. and Westbrook, W.F. (1980) *Human Costs of Flooding and Implementability of Non-structural Damage Reduction in the Tug Fork Valley of West Virginia*. Fort Belvoir, VA, USA: US Army Corps of Engineers

BCEOM (1990) *Dommages de crues (bassins de la Moselle)*. Paris, France: BCEOM

Boer, B.; Craig, D.; Handmer, J.W. and Ross, H. (1991) *The Potential Role of Mediation in the Resource Assessment Commission Inquiry Process*. Discussion Paper no. 1. Canberra, Australia: Resource Assessment Commission

Buck, W. (1988) *On Improved Flood Control Planning and Analysis of Flood Damage Data*. Paper given at the 39th IEC Meeting of the ICID. Dubrovnik

Chamberlaine, E.R.; Doube, L.; Milne, G.; Rolls, M. and Western, J.S. (1981) *The Experience of Cyclone Tracy*. Canberra, Australia: Australian Government Printing House

Cline, W. (1992) *The Economics of Global Warming*. Washington DC, USA: Institute of International Economics

Correia, F.C. (1987) Multivariate Partial Duration Series in Flood Risk Analysis. In Singh, V.P. (ed.) *Hydrologic Frequency Modelling*, 541–54. New York, USA: Reidel Publishing Company

Debizet, G. and Caude, G. (1986) *Simulation de dommages en zone urbaine mondiale: application au quartier de Sapiac*. Paris, France: Délégation aux Risques Majeurs

Debo, T.N. and Day, G.N. (1980) Economic Model for Urban Watersheds. *ASCE Journal of the Hydraulics Division*, 15333, 475–87

Delft Hydraulics (1989) *Criteria for Assessing Vulnerability to Sea Level Rise: a global inventory of high risk areas*. Report H838. Delft, Netherlands: Delft Hydraulics

Erikson, T. (1976) Loss of Communality at Buffalo Creek. *American Journal of Psychiatry*, 133 (3), 302–5

Folkman, S. and Lazarus, R.S. (1980) An Analysis of Coping in a Middle-aged Community Sample. *Journal of Health and Social Behaviour*, 21, 219–39

Fordham, M.H. (1992) *Choice and Constraint in Flood Hazard Mitigation: the environmental attitudes of flood plain residents and engineers*. Unpublished PhD thesis. London, UK: Middlesex University

Gleser, G.C.; Green, B.L. and Winger, C.W. (1981) *Prolonged Psychological Effects of Disaster: a study of Buffalo Creek*. New York, USA: Academic Press

Green, C.H. (1988) *The Relationship between Flooding, Stress and Health.* Paper given to the London meeting of the British Psychological Society

Green, C.H. (1993) *The Transferability of Flood Loss Estimation Data between Countries.* Report to SIEE. London, UK: Middlesex University, Flood Hazard Research Centre

Green, C.H.; Emery, P.J.; Penning-Rowsell, E.C. and Parker, D.J. (1985) *The Health Effects of Flooding: a survey at Uphill, Avon.* London, UK: Middlesex University, Flood Hazard Research Centre

Green, C.H. and Newsome, D. (1992) *Ethics and the Calculi of Choice.* Paper given at the Stockholm Water Symposium, 10–14 August 1992. London, UK: Middlesex University, Flood Hazard Research Centre

Green, C.H. and Penning-Rowsell, E.C. (1986) Evaluating the Intangible Benefits and Costs of a Flood Alleviation Proposal. *Journal of the Institution of Water Engineers and Scientists*, 40 (3), 229–48

Green, C.H. and Penning-Rowsell, E.C. (1989) Flooding and the Quantification of 'Intangibles'. *Journal of the Institution of Water and Environmental Management*, 3 (1), 27–30

Green, C.H. and Tunstall, S.M. (1991) The Evaluation of Water Quality Improvements by the Contingent Valuation Method. *Applied Economics*, 23, 1135–46

Green, C.H. and Tunstall, S.M. (1993) *The Ecological and Recreational Value of River Corridors: an economic perspective.* Paper given at the Ecological Basis for River Management Symposium, Leicester, UK

Greenaway, M.A. and Smith, D.I. (1983) *ANUFLOOD Field Guide.* Canberra, Australia: Centre for Resource and Environmental Studies, Australian National University

Grigg, N.S. and Helweg, O.J. (1975) State-of-the-art of Estimating Flood Damage in Urban Areas. *Water Resources Bulletin*, 11 (2), 379–90

Günther, W. (1987) *Schadensanalyse des Innhochwassers in August 1985 fur den Bereich der Gemeinde Krailburg.* Munich, Germany: Bayerisches Landesamt fur Wasserwirtschaft

Günther, W. and Schmidtke, R. (1988) Hochwasserschadensanalysen – Pilotuntersuchung über das Inn-Hochwasser im August 1985 (Flood Damage Analyses – Pilot Investigation on the River Inn Flood in August 1985). *Wasserwirtschaft*, 78 (2), 61–8

Handmer, J. W. and Penning-Rowsell, E.C. (eds) (1990) *Hazards and the Communication of Risk.* Aldershot, UK: Gower Technical Press

Hargest, K.W.; Freeman, A.S.; Scanlon, D.A.; Turner, R.K. and Bateman, I.N. (1991) *Environmental Appraisal: a review of monetary evaluation and other techniques.* Report to the Transport and Road Research Centre. Birmingham, UK: Rendel Planning

Health and Safety Executive (1988) *The Tolerability of Risk from Nuclear Power Stations.* London, UK: HMSO

Higgins, R.J. (1981) *An Economic Comparison of Different Flood Mitigation Strategies in Australia.* Unpublished PhD thesis. School of Civil Engineering, University of New South Wales

Higgins, R.J. and Robinson, D.K. (1980) *The Assessment of Urban Flood*

Damages. Paper given at the Symposium on Hydrology and Water Resources. Adelaide, Australia

Homan, A.G. and Waybur, B. (1960) *A Study of Procedure in Estimating Flood Damage to Residential, Commercial and Industrial Properties in California*. Merlo Park, CA, USA: Stanford Research Institute

Huerta, F. and Horton, R. (1978) Coping Behaviour of Elderly Flood Victims. *Gerontologist*, 18, 541–6

Keeney, R.L. and Raiffa, H. (1976) *Decisions with Multiple Objectives: preferences and value trade-offs*. New York, USA: John Wiley

Krutilla, J.V. and Fisher, A.C. (1975) *The Economics of Natural Environments*. Baltimore, USA: Johns Hopkins Press

Lazarus, R.S. (1966) *Psychological Stress and the Coping Process*. New York, USA: Academic Press

Lind, R.C. (1982) A Primer on the Major Issues Relating to the Discount Rate for Evaluating National Energy Options. In Lind, R.C. (ed.) *Discounting for Time and Risk in Energy Policy*. Washington DC, USA: Resources for the Future

Louviere, J.J. (1988) *Analyzing Decision Making: motive conjoint analysis*. Newbury Park, CA, USA: Sage Publications

Merkblatter zur Wasserwirtschaft (1989) *Wahl des bemessungshochwassers*. Hamburg, Germany: Paul Parey

Miller, J.A.; Turner, J.G. and Kimball, E. (1981) Big Thompson Flood Victims: one year later. *Family Relations*, 30, 111–16

Mitchell, R.C. and Carson, R.T. (1989) *Using Surveys to Value Public Goods: the contingent valuation method*. Washington DC, USA: Resources for the Future

Naess, A. (1993) The Deep Ecological Movement: some philosophical aspects. In Armstrong, S. and Botzler, R.G. (eds) *Environmental Ethics – Divergence and Convergence*. New York, USA: McGraw-Hill

National Institute of Mental Health (1979) *Crisis Intervention Programs for Disaster Victims in Smaller Communities*. Washington DC, USA: US Department of Health and Human Services

Newsome, D.W. and Green, C.H. (1993) *Economic Value of Changes to the Water Environment*. RID Note 37, Bristol, UK. National Rivers Authority

Nijkamp, P.; Rietveld, P. and Voogd, H. (1990) *Multicriteria Evaluation in Physical Planning*. Amsterdam: North Holland

Nijkamp, P. and Van Delft, A. (1977) Multicriteria Analysis and Regional Decisionmaking. *Studies in Applied Regional Science*, 8. Nijhoff, Leiden, Netherlands

Nordhaus, W.D. (1993) *Managing the Global Commons: the economics of climate change*. Cambridge, Mass, USA: Massachusetts Institute of Technology (MIT) Press

OECD (1993a) *Coastal Zone Management: integrated policies*. Paris, France: OECD

OECD (1993b) *Coastal Zone Management: selected case studies*. Paris, France: OECD

Parker, D.J. (1991) *The Damage-reducing Effects of Flood Warnings*. London, UK: Middlesex University, Flood Hazard Research Centre

Parker, D.J.; Green, C.H. and Thompson, P.M. (1987) *Urban Flood Protection Benefits: a project appraisal guide (The Red Manual)*. Aldershot, UK: Gower Technical Press

Parker, D.J. and Handmer, J. (1992) *Hazard Management and Emergency Planning:*

perspectives on Britain. London, UK: James and James

Parker, D.J.; Penning-Rowsell, E.C. and Green, C.H. (1983) *Swalecliffe Coast Protection Proposals: evaluation of potential benefits*. London, UK: Middlesex University, Flood Hazard Research Centre

Parker, D.J. and Tunstall, S.M. (1991) *Managing Flood Warning Systems: the United Kingdom experience*. Annual Conference of the Association of Floodplain Managers. Denver, Colorado, 11 June

Pearce, D.W. and Turner, R.K. (1990) *Economics of Natural Resources and the Environment*. New York, USA: Harvester Wheatsheaf

Pearce, D.W. and Warford, J.J. (1993) *World Without End*. New York, USA: Oxford University Press

Peerbolte, E.B. (1993) *Sea-level Rise and Safety*. Twente, Netherlands: University of Twente

Penning-Rowsell, E.C. and Chatterton, J.B. (1977) *The Benefits of Flood Alleviation: a manual of assessment techniques (The Blue Manual)*. London, UK: Gower/Saxon House

Penning-Rowsell, E.C.; Green, C.H.; Thompson, P.M.; Coker, A.M.; Tunstall, S.M.; Richards, C. and Parker, D.J. (1992a) *The Economics of Coastal Management: a manual of assessment techniques*. London, UK: Belhaven Press

Penning-Rowsell, E.C. and Handmer, J. (1988) Flood Hazard Management in Britain: a changing scene. *Geographical Journal*, 154 (2), 209–20

Penning-Rowsell, E.C.; Parker, D.J. and Harding, D.M. (1986) *Floods and Drainage: British policies for hazard reduction, agricultural improvement and wetland conservation*. London, UK: Allen and Unwin

Penning-Rowsell, E.C.; Peerbolte, B.; Correia, F.N.; Fordham, M.; Green, C.H.; Pflügner, W.; Rocha, J.; Saraiva, M.; Schmidtke, R.; Torterotot, J. and Van der Veen, A. (1992b) Flood Vulnerability Analysis and Climate Change: towards a European methodology. In Saul, A.J. (ed.) *Floods and Flood Management*. Dordrecht, Netherlands: Kluwer Academic Publishers

Poulshock, S.W. and Cohen, E.S. (1975) The Elderly in the Aftermath of a Disaster. *Gerontology*, 5, 357–61

Powell, B. and Penick, E. (1983) Psychological Distress Following a Natural Disaster: a one year follow-up of 98 flood victims. *Journal of Community Psychology*, 2, 269–76

Price, J. (1978) Some Age-related effects of the 1974 Brisbane Floods. *Australian and New Zealand Journal of Psychiatry*, 12, 55–8

River Planning Division (1990) *Investigation of River Economy*. Tokyo, Japan: River Bureau, Ministry of Construction

Rocha, J. (1988) *Erosao NA Serra Do Algarve Relatorio Final*. Relatorio LENEC 112/89

Saraiva, M. da G. (1987) *A Defesa contra Cheias e sua Inserçâo no ordenamento do Território: area metropolitana de Lisboa* (Flood Defence and Land Use Planning. Lisbon Metropolitan area). MSc thesis in Urban and Regional Planning. Lisbon, Portugal: UTL

Saul, A.J. (ed.) (1992) *Floods and Flood Management*. Dordrecht, Netherlands: Kluwer Academic Publishers

SIEE (1993) *Analyse Empirique de l'Apparition des Désordres et des Dommages résultant des différentes crues dans l'agglomeration continué d'Ile-de-France.* Report to Institution Interdépartementale des Barrages Réservoirs du Bassin de la Seine. Montpellier, France: Société d'Ingénierie pour l'Eau et l'Environnement

Torterotot, J.P. (1988) *Organisation et réalisation d'enquêtes sur les dommages dus aux inondations.* Noisy-le-Grand, France: CERGRENE

Torterotot, J.P.; Kauark-Leite, L.A. and Roche, P.A. (1992) Analysis of Individual Real-time Responses to Flooding and Influence on Damage to Households. In Saul, A.J. (ed.) *Floods and Flood Management.* Dordrecht, Netherlands: Kluwer Academic Publishers

Torterotot, J.P. and Roche, P.A. (1990) Evaluations socio-économiques pour la gestion du risque d'inondation. Paper given at the European Conference of Water Management, Paris, 4–6 December. In *La gestion de l'eau,* 481–90. Paris, France: Presses de l'Ecole Nationale des Ponts et Chaussées

Tunstall, S.M. and Bossman-Aggrey, P. (1988) *Waltham Abbey and Thornwood, Essex: an assessment of the effects of the flood of 29th July 1987 and the benefits of flood alleviation.* London, UK: Middlesex University, Flood Hazard Research Centre

US Water Resources Council (1983) *Economic and Environmental Principles and Guidelines for Water and Related Land Resources Implementation Studies.* Washington DC, USA: Department of the Interior

Walthern, P. (ed.) (1988) *Environmental Impact Assessment.* London, UK: Unwin Hyman

Ward, R. (1978) *Floods: a geographical perspective.* London, UK: Macmillan

Winterfeldt, D. von and Edwards, W. (1986) *Decision Analysis and Behavioural Research.* Cambridge, UK: Cambridge University Press

CHAPTER 4

Models for Flood Hazard Assessment and Management

Joachim Klaus, Walter Pflügner, Reinhard Schmidtke, Herman Wind and Colin Green

INTRODUCTION

This chapter describes a number of computer models that have been developed for assessing the magnitude of flood hazards faced by different communities in Europe, and the likely impacts of these floods when they occur in the future, perhaps in the context of changed climatic characteristics (IPCC 1992). The models also assess the benefits of flood alleviation, often with a monetary valuation, as a prelude or an input to a system of decision making about alternative flood mitigating options (Ministry of Agriculture, Fisheries and Food 1993, Beyene 1992). Some of these models investigate different options in some detail, while others leave that process to different institutional or political decision-making systems.

The history of the development of these models is varied, and reflects the nature of the institutions from which they have been developed, the data used in the process of hazard assessment and management, and the different decision-making contexts. Thus in our comparison of the different existing models, we find that the different characteristics of the models reflect the research approaches adopted, which have their different backgrounds and purposes. In addition, the nature of the models reflects the different national methods of decision making about flood alleviation, and flood alleviation standards, and the institutional context in which that decision making is placed within a specific country.

This chapter, therefore, first compares the different models

available in the different countries in Europe, with the view to identifying particular gaps that have arisen. Secondly, the chapter reviews
early developmental work at Middlesex University with an analysis of
the BOCDAM computer model, designed to model flood impacts at
both a regional and a local level. Thirdly, the chapter gives a detailed
account of the model development research under way in Germany,
which emphasises the analysis of flood impacts at a regional scale, and
which has hitherto been neglected. This regional level is emphasised
here, with an analysis of the BOCDAM computer model, since that
scale of analysis is now the focus of research in both Germany and the
Netherlands (Delft Hydraulics and Rijkswaterstaat 1991, Delft
Hydraulics 1992). In both the BOCDAM and the German examples,
brief case studies are presented of the types of results that can be
generated.

In this way, this chapter builds on the previous chapters on flood
hazard impacts, and forms a bridge between that area of scientific
enquiry and the development of policy options. Such policy option
research is then discussed in subsequent chapters, which are concerned with flood forecasting and warning systems, and the development of engineering schemes and their interface with the public.

A COMPARISON OF EXISTING MODELS

The context

The development and support of policy guidelines for flood hazard
assessment and management, and thereby the reduction of flood
vulnerability, is one of the key issues in European river and coastal
management today. The evaluation of data, models and policy instruments must lead the way to the goal of vulnerability reduction, and
the standardisation of models and policy instruments will assist in the
development of a Europe-wide strategy towards flood hazard
mitigation (World Coast Conference Organizing Committee 1993).

This evaluation of existing models for flood hazard assessment
complements an earlier analysis (Chatterton and Penning-Rowsell
1981, Penning-Rowsell *et al.* 1987), which compared model development in Britain with that in Australia and the United States. The
research literature contains many examples of flood damage models,
including those developed in the United States and Australia; examples
are Penning-Rowsell *et al.* (1987), Loucks (1992), Torterotot (1993),

Bailas and Loucks (1978), El-Jabi and Ronselle (1987), Plazak (1986). Most of these models have the aim of gauging the impact of floods upon vulnerable populations, as a precursor to – or including – decision-making sequences about flood mitigation (Günther and Schmidtke 1988).

The evaluation here of these models does not include a comparison of the models' results, since that would be too extensive and is generally contained within the references cited. We concentrate here, instead, on a comparison of the models' concepts, and the model comparison has been made on the basis of these concepts and the constituent parts of the models such as data input, flood extent forecasting, flood depth and duration modelling, the assessment of flood impacts and the selection of remedial actions. The various concepts are presented and the arguments for and against different models are discussed. Our aim in this respect is to provide insight into the concepts which are relevant to these hazard assessment and management processes, and the development of guidance to policy makers on the selection of different models and sub-models for a particular flood problem at a given site.

The models and their development

The models now available are listed in Table 4.1. They have been developed for specific flood problems and therefore the models have inherent similarities but also dissimilarities, depending on the particular aspect considered.

Table 4.1: Models compared in this chapter.

Name of model	Developed by	Development stage
BOCDAM	FHRC, England	Application stage
ESTDAM	FHRC, England	Application stage
ISOS	Delft Hydraulics, The Netherlands	Application stage
PSIGH	LNEC, PSIGH, Portugal	Development stage
CIFLUPEDE	CERGRENE, France	Prototype
RSA	Braschel and Schmitz, Germany	Conceptual stage

Similarities are found, for instance, in the space and time scales employed. In general all models can be applied to a relatively small area, such as a river basin sub-catchment, but few address large-scale problems and the macro-economic impacts that these can bring. In all cases the impacts of extreme events such as a major river flood or coastal storm surge are investigated, and in general the period of investigation is long relative to the duration of such an event and ranges from days and years to decades or centuries. As such some models can explore the impact of a single flood, while others are designed to explore the impact of a range of floods, such as those occurring during the design life of flood alleviation works.

The framework of analysis of decision support systems for flood hazard assessment consists of a number of interconnecting modules which can be traced in most of these models. An outline of such a framework is shown in Figure 4.1. Depending on the type of application and the phase of the project, modules may be included or left out. For example, in the initial stage of a project the emphasis is on problem formulation, collecting technical and non-technical data on floods and flood alleviation measures, and formulating the requirements with which the solution should comply. During progress on the project, forward and backward feedback loops are often required, leading to a much more complex scheme than shown in Figure 4.1. However, the simplicity contained in Figure 4.1 is designed to show the inherent similarities between the models that have so far been developed.

The central module in any conceptual framework for modelling flood hazard assessment and management (see Figure 4.1) is formed by the impact assessment of the floods. Flood impacts may range from the social loss (loss of lives) to the economic loss, loss of ecologically valuable land, loss of historic and heritage values and so on (Schmidtke 1993).

Surrounding this module on flood impact assessment are modules concerned with flood modelling, designed to determine the water extent and depth in any point in space as a function of geography, hydrology, hydraulics and hydrographics. In turn, the flood impact assessment module is followed by an analysis of different flood measures, including an analysis of the range of possible measures to be selected in any one location. Those modules can also contain routines designed to gauge the costs of the particular flood mitigation measure.

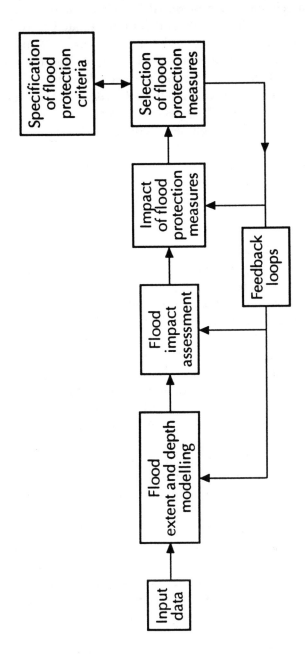

Figure 4.1: A theoretical framework for model comparison.

The data related to a specific flood problem – or a specific flood alleviation scheme – are provided by the input data module. This module contains all the data and routines related to the project or scheme: geographical data, hydrographic data, land use, historical and demographic data and so on. The module and the specification of the required flood protection measure describe, on the basis of flood protection policy being adopted, criteria which the proposed solution should satisfy. The selection of measures takes place on the basis of a comparison between flood impacts and required flood protection, with its associated cost, and the actual decision is not necessarily made within any one module shown in Figure 4.1 but can be made on the basis of data supplied by the modules and against the background of particular national laws and decision-making processes.

Model comparison

With regard to input data, experience with input handling of the various models shows that the preparation of the input data is a very time-consuming task in the module preparation phase.

From the point of view of modelling costs, therefore, progress can be made in this area by selecting the appropriate procedures, methods and aggregation levels. It should be noted that the type and contents of the input data are different for each of the models being compared, and the type and contents of the input data depend on the level of aggregation (principally whether a single property, a flur (Germany), a stretch of river or dike ring is employed). In none of the models is the level of aggregation and the required accuracy of the input data derived from output requirements. It would appear, therefore, that the selection of the level of aggregation is based on experience (i.e. the art of modelling) or the availability of data, rather than on scientific arguments.

In none of the modules – except the RSA approach discussed below – are flood-prone areas delimited in compliance with the administrative boundaries, and numerical data listings from field surveys or secondary sources are generally used as a data source. In the descriptions of the models cited in the references there are many suggestions as to the use of a geographic information systems (GIS) format, but so far the application of a GIS system has not proved a guarantee of time savings, although it greatly enhances the display of the results and this can be important for gaining public understanding and support (see Chapter 7).

With regard to flood extent forecasting, an analysis of the different flood forecasting modules within the models leads to the following conclusions. First, the hydrology or hydrographic analysis in the models is treated via input parameters, yielding for example flood volumes and flood durations. In only a few models is the actual build-up of flood waters taken to be relevant, and therefore in some respects the models are static rather than dynamic. Secondly, the failure of flood defence infrastructures (dikes, sluices, embankments, etc.) is represented in only four out of the six models. This is partly due to the fact that data on failing flood defence infrastructure are scarce and the mechanisms of failure are therefore inadequately treated within the models as so far developed.

The hydraulic analysis in the models is reduced to simple flood frequency curves. An exception is the PSIGH model (see Chapter 7), in which the flood flow is modelled using friction laws. It may be the case, as a background to the way that flood modelling is undertaken within the hazard assessment systems, that there is an underlying hypothesis that sufficient accuracy in the output can be achieved without detailed flow modelling. The PSIGH model could be used to test this hypothesis in relation to the results from other models.

As indicated above, the module on flood impacts is essential to all these models. Table 4.2 lists the types of impacts investigated, and this shows how many impacts are ignored and how different models are selective as to what they as yet consider.

Most of these models contain routines incorporating flood damage data. One of the lessons learned in analysing the damage data contained within these models is that there is a considerable scatter in the data, if they are comparable at all (see Chapter 3). This suggests the hypothesis that damage data depend on some important and independent variables (e.g. the ability to move inventory items in reaction to flood threat, the degree of awareness, the appropriateness of counter-flood behaviour, the expectation of compensation, etc.). This scatter in the data also forms an important source of uncertainty as far as hazard assessment and decision making is concerned (Günther and Niekamp 1989).

Regarding the modules within the models on the selection of flood mitigation measures, these modules require a criterion to be

Table 4.2: Land use and economic data used in the models compared here.

	Impact categories			
	Properties	Agriculture; industry	Ecology	Infra-structure
CIFLUPEDE	Average values	Average values	Not included	Not included
PSIGH	Not included	Not included	Not included	Not included
ISOS	National average values	National average values	National average values	Not included
BOCDAM	Average values	Average values	Not included	Not included
ESTDAM	Individual prop	Not included	Not included	Included
RSA	National average values	Average per town	Not included	Not included

established on the basis of which selection can be made. Several alternative approaches are possible. First, there is the identification of flooded areas and the resulting damage potentials. Secondly, certain modules may imply a compliance to a norm or standard of frequency of overtopping. Thirdly, models can use a simple benefit-cost analysis (BCA) framework, simply comparing monetary damages with costs of mitigation measures; and, finally, some modules may employ a multi-criteria analysis and thereby attempt to incorporate more than just economic considerations.

In the first of these alternatives, additional information on the acceptable level of flood damages and the cost of remedial actions is required before remedial measures can be selected. This is the case in the RSA, CIFLUPEDE and the PSIGH models. The ISOS model (Chapter 5) belongs to the second category identified above. In that case an optimal flood hazard management strategy can be determined with reference to pre-existing flood protection standards. Such an approach contrasts with those in the second and third categories listed above, to which the ESTDAM/BOCDAM models belong.

Our research has reviewed the advantages and disadvantages of the BCA approach and the multi-criteria analysis approach to providing decision support methods for flood hazard management. The main criticism of the BCA approach is that it oversimplifies by transforming all effects of the project into monetary terms. The characteristic of multi-criteria analysis is the explicit stating of natural units for the different criteria; a weight vector is needed to reflect the priorities of the objectives. It is argued (Van der Veen and Wierstra 1993) that the problem of BCA is shifted to the determination of the subjective weight vector in multi-criteria analysis.

Because important progress is being made in the field of the valuation of public goods, for instance with the contingent valuation method, some important drawbacks of BCA seem to be being reduced or eliminated. Hence we conclude that there is an increasing preference for BCA as a decision support method for flood hazard management, although the decision makers should be made aware of its limitations.

An important factor in the comparison of these models is the accuracy achieved by different means. In the BOCDAM model the point concerning the aggregation level and accuracy in the input data is taken as an issue in its own right. In the flood impact module of the RSA model (see below) the step towards a BCA framework is not made, because it is argued that the probability of flooding caused by system failure with regard to the existing defences is not known with sufficient accuracy to allow the incorporation of this approach. In the CIFLUPEDE model the uncertainty in various data sources and in the model itself is analysed in order to investigate the effect on the output obtained. In the ISOS study the uncertainty in the variables on the dike-raising has been investigated, in the form of sensitivity analysis.

Some initial conclusions
Although all the flood hazard assessment and management models evaluated here more or less comply with the framework given in Figure 4.1, it is clear that we are some way away from developing a commonly accepted flood hazard management tool. Different concepts are being used in different models and it will be important in future to clarify these differences.

In the area of uncertainty only very tentative first steps have been taken. One of the challenging statements in the field is the hypothesis being developed with the RSA model concerning the lack of accuracy of the estimates of the probability of failure of existing flood infrastructures. The suggested consequences of this uncertainty on the modelling approach itself obviously requires further study. The CIFLUPEDE study raises the question as to whether the computation-intensive Monte Carlo simulation is required, or whether a linearised error analysis would be sufficient. If such a linearised approach works satisfactorily, this would lead to more transparency and probably time saving in the error analysis.

What this model comparison reveals is considerable differences in tackling broadly similar flood hazard assessment problems. While these differences can be attributed to the historical origins of the models and the nature of the decision framework in which they were constructed, there must be concern about the reasons for them and the possible lack of consistency. Of particular concern is the difficulty being experienced in the development of regional scale analysis, since that level of analysis inherently involves greater error and can include greater expense in data collection. This is one reason why our research has taken us into the field of regional scale analysis, with both the reappraisal of the BOCDAM system and the development of the RSA model. Both these aspects are discussed further below.

MULTIPLE-LEVEL FLOOD ASSESSMENT MODELS: EXPERIENCE FROM THE UNITED KINGDOM

This section describes a range of flood loss evaluation methods, models and data sets – developed primarily in the United Kingdom – designed to estimate the economic impacts of urban flood alleviation and drainage projects. The assessment methods and data described here have already been used extensively by water authorities, local authorities and consulting engineers in the United Kingdom (Penning-Rowsell and Chatterton 1977, Parker *et al.* 1987).

The need for multiple levels of appraisal
A wide range of urban flood protection and drainage projects need to be appraised, at markedly different scales, so that methods are required at a variety of planning levels (Table 4.3). We have simplified this situation down to three levels or scales of appraisal. Computer models and data sets have been devised for each.

Level 1 Investment priority setting. Data and methods are required, first, to determine which flood alleviation projects out of a range of

Table 4.3: Multi-level modelling methods available in the United Kingdom for evaluating the benefits and costs of urban flood protection projects.

Requirement/ purpose	Appraisal system	Data needs	Estimation accuracy	Relative study cost (%)
1. Priority-setting level	BOCDAM	Low, limited	Low but reliable for purpose	10-20
2. Project feasibility level	ESTDAM simple mode	Relatively low for purpose	High and reliable	40-70
3. Full project feasibility level	ESTDAM intensive mode	High: data for purpose	High and very reliable	100

possible projects covering a large area, such as an entire catchment or a metropolitan region, are likely to generate the largest benefits in excess of costs and be most socially desirable. Secondly, we need to determine whether any engineering solution to a flood problem in a particular area is likely to be economically viable.

Thus, a 'high level' method is needed to 'scan' the various investment possibilities, to identify those investment opportunities likely to produce the greatest return from society's investment, and to provide the basis for devising a phased series of more detailed evaluations suitable for a continuing programme of capital investment in flood protection.

Level 2 The project feasibility investigation. Assessment methods are required which focus on individual projects to investigate in detail the likely benefits and costs of specific flood protection proposals, and to evaluate alternative project designs and standards of flood protection. Such methods use more accurate and reliable hydraulic, hydrographic and economic data than in level-1-type investigations.

Level 3 Full scheme feasibility investigation. Once a decision has been made to pursue a project, further studies may be required to provide more detailed estimates of scheme benefits and costs, particularly to optimise design standards in sub-areas within the overall study area, and the results may be of use in managing the project in terms of phasing its implementation.

The appraisals required for each level may be undertaken as one-off exercises in data collection and hand calculation. However, a range of computer models have been devised and these, with national or region-wide databases, can greatly reduce appraisal problems while increasing reliability and consistency, especially in large studies. These data and models are discussed below.

Flood damage data systems
The main effect of flood protection is flood damage avoidance. Flood losses may be categorised into direct, indirect and intangible. Direct flood damages are those caused by the physical contact of flood water with damageable property. Indirect flood losses are those caused through interruption and disruption of economic and social activities, usually as a consequence of direct flood damages. Intangible flood losses are the unevaluated losses. They can be direct or indirect, and include anxiety, stress, ill-health, loss of life and personal disruption as a consequence of flooding.

Extensive data sets have been developed by the Flood Hazard Research Centre for estimating, in the British context, the potential direct and indirect flood losses avoided by flood protection, using synthetically constructed depth-damage data sets for standard property types commonly found in flood-prone areas (see Penning-Rowsell and Chatterton 1977, Parker *et al.* 1987, Suleman *et al.* 1988). These flood damage data sets are designed for use in conjunction with the BOCDAM and ESTDAM computer models described below to evaluate the benefits of any urban flood protection project in the United Kingdom.

Evaluating intangible flood losses is more problematic (Chapter 3) but important advances in assessing the health and other social impacts of floods on householders have also been made in the past (Green and Penning-Rowsell 1985) and have also been alluded to herein in Chapter 3. Whilst the British flood damage data are not necessarily transferable to other countries, the principles and methods of flood loss assessment, computational procedures and software, and the methods of constructing synthetic flood depth-damage data sets are directly transferable, and have been used in Australia and transferred for comparative research purposes to parts of Germany (Beyene 1992).

The construction of synthetic direct flood damage data sets must be clearly based on theoretically sound economic evaluation principles, which have been translated into simple generalised rules and formulae (Parker *et al.* 1987). For example, direct flood damage costs should relate to restoration of property to average pre-flood conditions rather than replacement costs, since the latter overestimates the economic resource loss from flooding. In estimating flood losses, transfer payments should be removed to reveal true economic values. For example, subsidies and some taxes must be identified and netted out to determine the resource costs of both the flooding and, conversely, the flood alleviation project.

Direct flood damage (Penning-Rowsell and Chatterton 1977) and subsequent disruption to urban economies (Parker *et al.* 1987) often lead to 'knock-on' or secondary impacts. These multiplier effects may be important in major urban areas, and econometric modelling methods are needed in such cases to model secondary effects. Often, however, the negative secondary (multiplier) impact of flooding on an urban economy – such as loss of production – will be partly offset by a temporary increase in replacement expenditure following flooding which helps to restore regional or national income.

In addition, moreover, the local losses of trade and business consequent upon flooding may only result in deferred business, or gains of trade and business elsewhere within the economy. These local business losses are therefore mostly financial rather than economic losses and hence they should not be counted within a national economic efficiency BCA. Thus, calculating the benefits of flood protection investments is different at national, regional and local scales. National economic impacts will be less than regional impacts, which in turn will be less than local impacts. Flood loss data need to reflect these distributional and local impacts of flood protection at different scales.

Appraisal systems and models: early work on BOCDAM as a prototype regional model

BOCDAM is a level 1 computer model (see above) which calculates estimated flood damage potential in river reaches or specified areas for flood events of specified magnitudes (Green *et al.* 1987). The expected value of flood damages and present value calculations are performed separately within a pre-formatted spreadsheet program BENAL using the flood event damage results from BOCDAM.

The BOCDAM program is designed for situations where there are limited resources for undertaking detailed hydrologic, hydraulic and engineering investigations of project feasibility. Its usefulness is at a maximum where a preliminary estimate of the economic viability of flood protection may be needed for a number of locations within a large catchment or urban area. The model is particularly useful where limited resources generate the need to prioritise projects in order to protect some areas before others, based on economic optimisation (Table 4.3), and where very large urban areas are involved for which a level 2 or level 3 analysis would be prohibitively expensive.

BOCDAM is therefore most useful as a 'high level' priority-setting technique which is used to devise a programme of capital investment within which there will be a number of projects each of which will require further detailed evaluation. Part of the value of BOCDAM lies in the ability of the method to determine whether it is likely to be worthwhile collecting further data necessary for project design, and whether it is worthwhile undertaking individual 'project specific' engineering and economic feasibility investigations, the latter using the RSA regional model or the ESTDAM urban flood benefit assessment model (see below).

Deliberately, therefore, BOCDAM has limited data input requirements (Table 4.4). The system uses readily available cross-sectional topographic data and Monte Carlo methods to generate synthetic patterns of development in terms of property type, location, area and floor level. Estimates taken from plans of the percentage of the area which is developed for different land uses are used to generate patterns of development, while valley cross-section data are the basis for the generation of synthetic floor levels. Simplified sets of data on flood damage potential for principal types of development are incorporated into the system.

The results from BOCDAM
An application of BOCDAM to the middle Thames catchment (approximately 40 km of river) to the west of London, England,

Table 4.4: A comparison of data sources for BOCDAM and ESTDAM.

Type of data	BOCDAM	ESTDAM
Land use Categories Locations	Up to 10 Allocated to nearest cross-section	10 to 500 Detailed grid reference
Property: area and number Property levels	Estimate from plans Study area cross-sections then Monte Carlo technique to generate typical pattern of development relative to level	Field survey plus plans Property-by-property assessment based on maps and field survey
Damage data Depth-damage data (direct and indirect damages)	Per area of development, values for each category for 3-15 depths - standard data only	Per property/area values for each category for 5 - 15 depths - standard data plus site surveys of damage potential in selected major sites
Traffic disruption Utility outages	Not assessed Not assessed	SROAD, PRO program Extra loss figures per non-flooded property affected
Hydrologic/hydraulic data Flood stages	Previous flood outlines then interpolate other events, resulting in flood elevations per cross-section	Detailed hydraulic study resulting in flood surface/profile
Probabilities	Expert estimate of likely exceedance probabilities of created events plus sensitivity analysis	Detailed hydrological assessment of exceedance probabilities - past events plus records

illustrates the benefit estimation results of a BOCDAM analysis (Figures 4.2, 4.3 and Table 4.5) (Green *et al.* 1987), which may then be compared with alternative project costs and capital availability.

BOCDAM is explicitly designed to use imprecise data and hence the output contains greater uncertainties than with more data-intensive methods, such as ESTDAM; BOCDAM itself also identifies the importance of these uncertainties. The results appear to be sufficiently reliable both to indicate where further appraisals are worthwhile, and to identify where the available resources should be concentrated in subsequent investigations.

In this respect it is interesting to record that following the early work on the prototype BOCDAM program, the results of which are shown in Figures 4.2 and 4.3, more detailed appraisals have been undertaken by the National Rivers Authority, using the Middlesex University ESTDAM model. Analyses have been undertaken for both Maidenhead and the Staines area (shown in Figure 4.2), and these were chosen because they indicated in the BOCDAM results that here was the maximum potential for benefits to be obtained from flood alleviation works.

It is notable that the detailed results follow the same rank order as the BOCDAM results, but the calculated benefits are approximately twice as great. Thus for Maidenhead the benefits of flood alleviation amount to some £40 million whereas for Staines the results indicate benefits of approximately £60 million. In both cases a substantial amount of benefit is obtained from above the design standard flood return period, since the schemes envisaged are either by-pass channels or channel enlargements. Be that as it may, this does not detract from the value of the regional scale analysis (RSA) undertaken by BOCDAM, which was instrumental in focusing attention on those two particular reaches, the results for which from detailed analysis followed the pattern established by the BOCDAM prototype results.

The problems with BOCDAM are both technical and 'political'. First, the efficiency of flood damage estimation is dependent on the availability of at least medium-quality maps or ortho-photographs of the area to be flooded, while the results are also dependent on estimates within the data input process of the percentage of urban development within any one valley cross-section area. In addition, the final results depend on the estimates it is necessary to make of the return period at which overbank flooding and damage begins, as well as the location of the outer edge of the flood plain and its associated return period of flooding.

The 'political' problems with BOCDAM, as with any pre-feasibility study technique, are that interested parties will tend to assume that the results from this very simple model will approximately represent

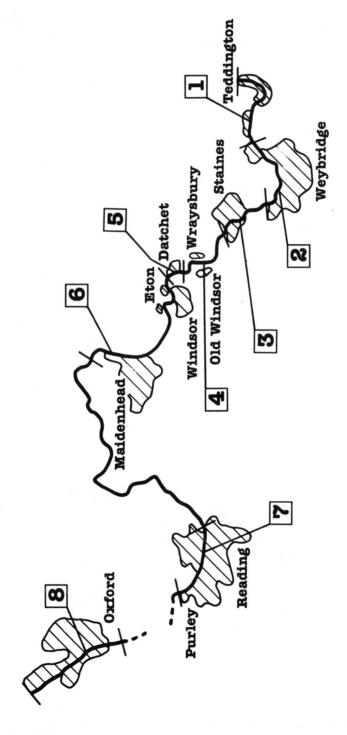

Figure 4.2: The area of the lower Thames catchment, United Kingdom, where the BOCDAM model was tested.

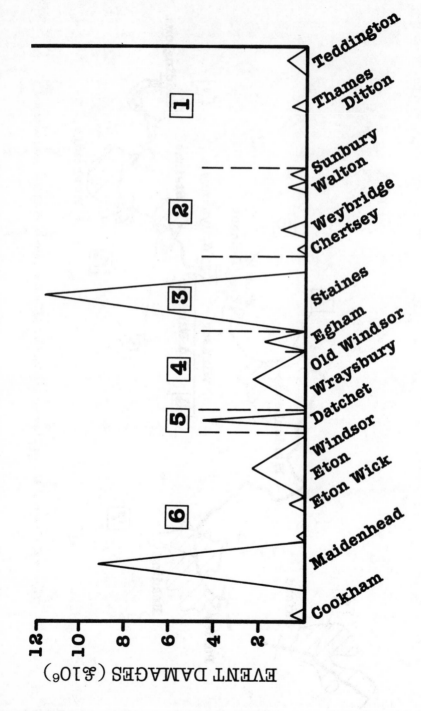

Figure 4.3: Summary results of BOCDAM analysis for the middle reaches of the Thames between Maidenhead and London (Teddington).

Table 4.5: A summary of BOCDAM results (flood protection benefits) for the middle Thames valley, England.

Reach	Cross sections used (number)	Urban area (hectares)	Number of residential properties in area	Event loss: 1947 equivalent flood (£M)* (see Fig 4.3)	Net Present Value £M**		
					Optimistic	Pessimistic	Final
Teddington	12	17.60	1032	1.97	1.1	1.9	1.5
Chertsey	14	20.85	1805	3.13	2.0	3.5	2.8
Staines	16	92.67	8595	11.80	3.5	5.4	4.9
Windsor	14	28.36	3328	9.39	3.5	5.5	4.6
Dorney	2	4.74	853	1.05	0.5	0.9	0.8
Maidenhead	12	37.95	4448	9.63	6.1	11.7	8.8

* Only two river stages were available for this analysis: bankfull and the major flood of 1947. Further flood stages are interpolated and equivalent return periods were assumed as follows:

ESTIMATED RETURN PERIOD OF EVENT (years)

Optimistic	5	12	30	75
Pessimistic	2	8	20	50
Final	10	15	20	50 (the last, the 1947 flood stage plus 100mm)

** NPV of benefits is calculated for a 50 year project life using the then standard UK 5 per cent discount rate.

the final results from more detailed investigations. Thus, flood alleviation benefits of, say, £10 million will be interpreted as providing
sufficient justification for a major engineering scheme, whereas the
final results from more detailed modelling could be as low as one
twentieth of (or conversely, five times) that sum. Expectations tend to be
created by the pre-feasibility results which may prove to be unfounded.

The need for model development

This chapter, so far, has indicated the types of models developed and
undertaken to date, and some of the results. This shows that there is
considerable national diversity in the approaches undertaken, and
that the results obtained at the regional scale and the local scale differ
significantly.

Considerable confidence remains with the local scale analysis, but
the regional scale of analysis is highly problematic. What the approach
needs is a model which is simple to operate, non-demanding as to
data inputs, yet gives results which have a degree of reliability in terms
of their prediction of the results from more detailed analysis with
better data and modelling. This, of course, is an ambitious aim.

Nevertheless, we have pursued the objective of enhancing the
sophistication of regional scale modelling in our research, and this is
outlined below in a case study largely concerned with Germany. We
have put our emphasis on this regional scale because we believe that
too much attention is unnecessarily devoted to detailed studies in
advance of a clear picture of the broad nature and scale of the hazard
that is being analysed. With better RSA we can determine priorities
more accurately, by targeting more carefully the detailed investigations
that should come later, and also link more specifically to regional
planning rather than project appraisal.

Enhancing regional scale analysis: research on the RSA model

Following the developments of the BOCDAM model, which in itself is
very crude, we can see that the sustainable use and development of
flood plain areas calls for a more comprehensive decision support
system, taking into account all the economic and environmental
impacts as well as the implications for social welfare. The search for
such solutions can reveal major internal conflicts between these

variables and therefore sophisticated planning and evaluation tools are needed (Deutscher Verband für Wasserwirtschaft und Kulturbau 1985). In order to apply these and cope with the complex questions involved, future policies for integrated planning of flood plain and coastal zone areas need an adequate information base (Klaus 1984, Klaus and Schmidtke 1990, Council of the European Communities 1992).

Research questions and agenda

We can now see that the standard micro-economic appraisals of single flood defence projects are mainly based on a property-by-property approach, calculating damage values from each property in the flood plain area and processing this information in a traditional BCA.

Without doubt, some components of such model structures can be applied to larger areas, such as those that need to be considered in strategic regional planning of flood plain areas and coastal zones. However, here is where difficulties can arise, due to the following problems and methodological considerations. First, since very large numbers of data sets have to be collected at a broad scale, effective field survey is likely to be too expensive, as well as too time consuming. Secondly, many individuals are unwilling to reveal the necessary personal data required in micro-economic studies (particularly in relation to industrial site surveys), especially in so far as this information affects the competitive positions of the industries concerned. The alternative way of collecting data from other authorities and government institutions will also often fail because of legal restrictions concerning data protection. Thirdly, owing to economic and other linkages, not all the adverse effects of flooding can be related to a single property itself, not least because some linkages occur to activities outside its locality and region.

This has led us to focus, as discussed above, on the need for different approaches for different scales in flood protection on coastal zone decision making. RSA calls for a meso-scale evaluation approach which satisfies the methodological requirements and takes into account, for the sake of efficiency, the need for aggregated data. An important point here is that the data we require do not exist ready to be collected. We need some procedures to derive these data from existing official statistics; that is by far the best starting point rather than field data collection.

A sophisticated approach must take into account the whole pattern and functionalities within the economy of the area concerned. All flood-related damage and losses will be of interest, whether they are suffered by groups of inhabitants or economic activities over the different sectors of activity.

The main ideas underlining the model being developed are as follows. First, different flooding scenarios need to be analysed for their damage potential and other impacts. We need to get results at a higher level of spatial resolution, but with a full sector disaggregation facility. The essentials of the system developed are that property values within administratively and geographically well-defined areas will be derived from official statistics (as, for example, obtained from national accounting and census returns). These property values will be broken down by particular sectors.

Secondly, property damage related to specific flood scenarios goes to show the relative impact of different flood scenarios on different sectors of the economy. Thirdly, by adding the losses of value added, and the emergency costs involved in flood events, the total amount of flood damage with the different flood scenarios can be analysed. In this way, finally, the RSA becomes a decision support system which serves all interests within the flood plain area and beyond, and highlights the need for strategic land use planning there. Only in this way will this planning lead to the optimal mix between flood alleviation measures and land use restrictions in the hazardous areas.

Input variables

The starting point for evaluating the effectiveness of flood defence schemes at a regional scale is the natural flood conditions as they currently exist. These conditions result from the interaction of the topography of the area and the exposure to storm surge or inland flood events. Both components need to be quantified according to clear and well-known procedures.

To identify physical risks, the land units involved have to be classified according to their altitude and size. In doing this we need to balance the needs for a high level of spatial resolution, owing to the geographical specificity of floods, with the need for the kind of overview essential at a regional scale. At a more detailed level we might have to model the effects of failure of existing flood defence systems, in the form of breaches or other damage to flood infrastructure. However, our practical experience shows that such calculations are largely speculative. This is particularly true when looking at the possibility of breaching of flood defences from major floods when such defences are based on designs related to events with shorter return periods. Therefore, our RSA gives preference to the use of a scenario method which ignores local flooding mechanisms.

The assumption here is that there is a systems failure and that this leads to a set of scenarios with different volumes of water flowing into the impact area, resulting in different inundations according to morphology. This assumption is similar to that used in BOCDAM, and means that local detail may be of low accuracy but the overall results should be sound, in the interests of preserving the integrity of the RSA.

In the second main database are the elements describing physical impacts, discussed above, and this relates to socio-economic values and economic activities. The need is to have data with which to model the economic impacts of the floods as they occur in different areas within the region, whilst balancing the need for the appropriate level of local accuracy with the regional integrity of the model as a high level decision aid.

The problem with the socio-economic dimension is choosing which data to collect and in which manner these data can be disaggregated down to the land unit level chosen. For the elements chosen in Table 4.6, five groups are of major importance for the purpose in hand: the population that can be protected, houses, the number employed, productive capital stock and other property values, and the value added by different industries.

Available official statistics have, in each case, to be analysed to derive the data needed. For these purposes, methods of disaggregation of these official statistics have had to be found. The first step here is to identify the possibilities of sub-dividing the economic activities into sectors, for which a compromise between data homogeneity and data availability is needed. The second step concerns the spatial location aspect. For example, the total property value for a particular industry can be derived using the sector-specific capital intensity figures (i.e. the ratio of capital invested per person employed) and the geographical pattern of employed persons.

The development of the model involves overlaying the regional pattern of sectoral productive and consumptive capital values with the

Table 4.6: The basic elements of the RSA economic classification (Klaus and Schmidtke 1990).

A   Socio-economic base
    1.   Population
        1.1   status and long-term development
        1.2   age pattern
    2.   Housing
        2.1   residential houses, flats, residents
        2.2   housing capital stock
    3.   Infrastructure
        3.1   education, recreation
        3.2   power supply and environmental services
        3.3   traffic and communication

B   Sites and factors of production
    1.   Production plants and workplaces
        1.1   employers and employees in the economic sectors
        1.2   size of production places
    2.   Land as a factor of production
        2.1   land use categories and shares
        2.2   values of built up and agricultural land
    3.   Productive capital stock and other property values of economic sectors
        3.1   gross capital invested
        3.2   stocks and other values

C   Current results of economic activities
    1.   Gross value added
    2.   Tax revenue

D   Environmental assets
    1.   Environmental structures
    2.   Conservation areas and other protected areas

specific pattern of flood-proneness, and this results in a pattern of socio-economic values and activities at risk from the hazard. These results will show the damage potentials of the different industries concerned, related to the different inundation scenarios being considered. Once this information is obtained there exist many possibilities of aggregating this information to land units at a higher level, or to the level of the industry and sector itself as a whole.

Micro-economic analysis uses depth-damage functions for different land uses and calculates damages for each property (Chapter 3) (Günther and Niekamp 1989). An analogous approach here has to be used at the meso-scale. Depth-damage functions are substituted by matrices for the different categories of productive and consumptive capital. Such matrices show the relationship between inundation depth and the percentage of damage to the total value of the asset. This method differs substantially from the micro-economic tools discussed above because there no information is given about the total value of the assets from which damage potential is calculated.

Intersecting the spatial pattern of the damage potentials with the damage matrices for the different flooding scenarios results in the region-specific pattern of damage values. Area-specific and activity-specific aggregations, again, are possible in a wide range of different ways. With this information it is quite simple to establish the value of property at risk from flooding for each particular sector against the water level scenarios (Figure 4.4). The results in Figure 4.4 show which kinds of property values are involved and to what extent they are endangered, depending on different flood scenarios (here related to flood depth).

With regard to the estimation of damages according to different sectors and the different scenarios, numerical integration leads to spatially distributed, sector and scenario-specific damage information, which can be aggregated and displayed in many different ways. An overall result is shown in Figure 4.5, which gives the total amount of damage according to different flooding scenarios for different types of land. Combining the information in Figures 4.4 and Figure 4.5 gives damage potential for the region as a percentage of the property value at risk.

The results of the overall analysis

In this exercise we are trying to calibrate the extent of vulnerability of differently scaled activities to flooding. Applying decision theory, we need to look at the trade-offs between different decision scenarios (Klaus *et al.* 1981, Pflügner 1988). One very important trade-off has to consider, at the overall level, the resources necessary to compensate the natural hazards of regions being exposed to floods. Such an investigation can be called comparative overall analysis.

With this approach, the essential information on the benefits side applies to the totality of socio-economic values which are protected by the flood defence scheme under consideration. With the model development we have undertaken, such an overall analysis now becomes feasible (Figure 4.6). The topographic and other natural conditions of the region concerned, together with the flood event pattern it suffers on the one hand, and the investment strategy on the

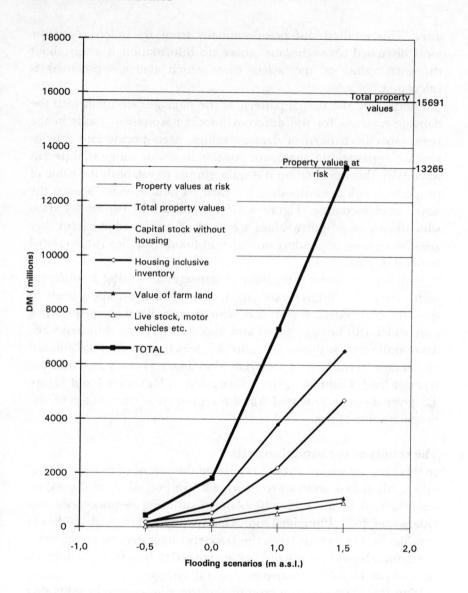

Figure 4.4: Property values at risk from flooding in specified sectors and from different flood scenarios.

other, are the main determinants surrounding decisions about each flood protection scheme. For these determinants quantitative values can be derived using existing data; the question is which set of socio-economic quantities allows a sufficient judgement to be made

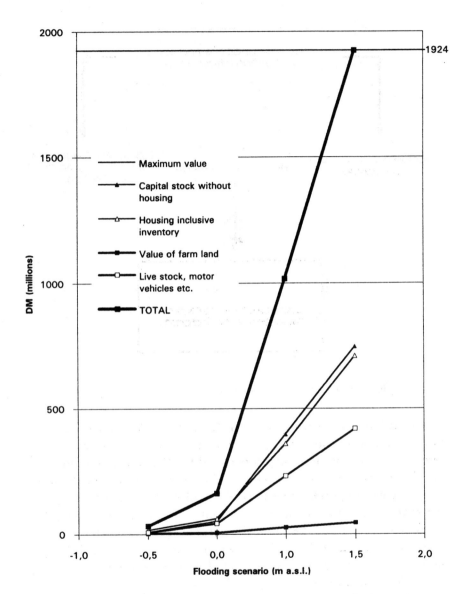

Figure 4.5: Damage to property in specified sectors and from different flood scenarios.

concerning the total protected values.

As we have discussed previously (Chapter 3), the comparison of the costs of particular safety measures and the value of the property to be protected gives an overall picture of the cost-effectiveness of the

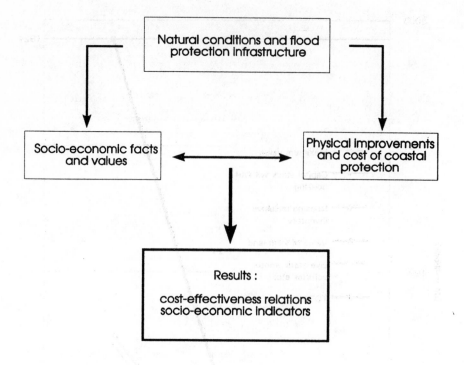

Figure 4.6: Regional Scale Analysis: system diagram.

works, and we can quantify that in different ways. We can look at it in terms of the protection costs per capita, per person employed or per unit of currency of different property values. Possible benefit figures of this kind can be set in relation to other national economic figures, such as gross regional product of the region under study, the sum invested in the budgets of the different communities involved, the investment budget of the authorities in charge of flood protection, and so on. Linking such data enables comparison to be made between different parts of regions endangered by flooding and between different regions themselves.

The level of systems analysis
Our goal in RSA is to obtain a high resolution for different sectors of economic activity, as well as high spatial resolution.

In the application of the RSA approach to Germany, there was no problem with regard to land use. The national land register provides all land use data for all single properties according to a complex classification involving thirty-eight categories. However, the possibility of disaggregating statistical economic values down to that detailed level is restricted because of methodological limitations and lack of reported data.

An innovative approach to this impasse had to be adopted. A satisfactory compromise could be found by basing the spatial resolution of RSA not on single properties but on the next higher level of land units. This involved, in Germany, an aggregate of some fifty to one hundred properties according to the German procedure of land registering (in German: *Fluren*). This is the second level in the German land classification, one up from the individual properties.

Using the spatial pattern of population and of employment respectively as indicators of the geography of economic activities, it was possible to obtain the information needed on capital values according to the following nine sectors:

1. Farmland
2. Livestock
3. Agriculture (productive capital stock, housing excluded)
4. Industries (productive capital stock, housing excluded)
5. Commerce and services (productive capital stock, housing excluded)
6. Transportation, infrastructure and communication (productive capital stock, housing excluded)
7. Value of stocks
8. Housing (inventory included)
9. Motor vehicles

The structure of the data input in this way determines the way of processing data in RSA and the possibility of cross-sectioning data within the decision support system for assessing damage potentials and flood damage respectively for individual sectors.

CASE STUDY TEST OF REGIONAL SCALE ANALYSIS IN GERMANY

To demonstrate the applicability of the RSA approach, results are taken from a case study (see map, Figure 4.7). This is a pilot investigation, and the findings are useful only for optimising the viability of the model. Nevertheless, besides this very important feedback, the empirical case study gives insight into the actual magnitude of flood risks that low-lying coastal zones have to face.

The case study area and its results

Our investigation has been of a flood defence system in a district of Germany at the North Sea coast which covers some 700 km², 25 per cent of which is below sea level and 86 per cent of which is lower than +1.5 m above sea level with a normal tide at about +2.0 m above sea level. The scheme as established consists of 124 km of embankment (66 km sea wall, 38 km of tidal river embankment, 20 km of inland embankment behind a storm surge barrier). The area has 76,100 inhabitants in seven communities and the industrial employment total is 30,900 people.

As usual, the institutional character of such an area is very complex. There are many different authorities working together, each of which is different in terms of its geographical scope and sectoral function. Thus, for example, the federal and state governments give grants for investment within the area. The state government is in charge of giving its approval for major projects, whereas local water authorities plan the projects and supervise their construction. Water associations are in charge of operating and maintaining the flood defence structures, while five water boards operate nearly 1,300 km of drainage ditches and channels.

This situation shows the difficulty of developing and managing flood mitigation projects, and emphasises the need for clear information on which all can base the planning and decision processes involved. For testing the model different flood scenarios were used ranging from inundating the areas below −0.5 m above sea level (35 km² affected) up to +1.5 m above sea level (600 km² affected). The spatial resolution of the model is based on 357 *Fluren*, which give a mean size of each land unit of approximately 2 km². This, then, is the basic building block of the RSA here. In built-up areas these land units are smaller geographically and in the open rural areas they are larger, a fact that improves the results substantially by giving more detail where there is greater flood damage potential. RSA allowed us to establish the values of property at risk for each of the nine specific sectors listed above for the different flooding scenarios chosen, as can be seen in an aggregated form in Figure 4.5 as well as in the total

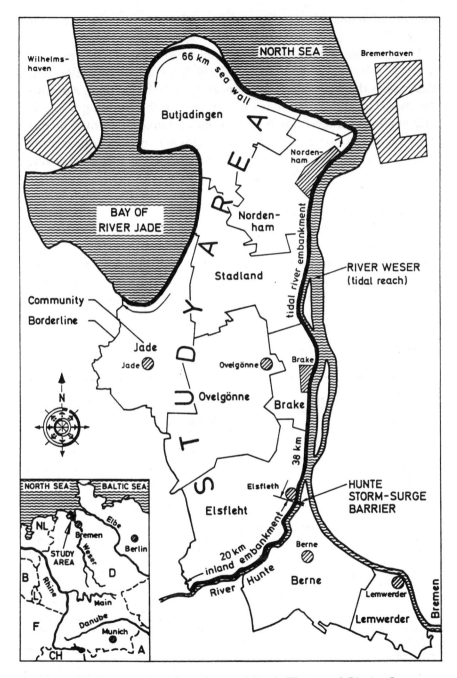

Figure 4.7: Location map of the study area within the Wesermarsch District, Germany.

amount of damage according to the different scenarios, given in Table 4.7.

The total property values within the existing defence scheme total nearly DM 16 billion, 85 per cent of which are at risk from flooding. This makes the total value at risk more than DM 13 billion. Applying the model results in the damage figures for the flooding scenario +1.5 m above sea level; the total amount of damage potential including the loss of value added and the emergency services costs is more than DM 2 billion. Table 4.7 gives the breakdown by sector according to the total property values, the value at risk and the damage potential. The highest values are associated with housing (35.5%), followed by commerce and services (22.9%).

Comparing the percentages of property values and values at risk, one can see a very similar pattern. This demonstrates that there is very little risk aversion in the development of these low-lying areas, and that land use planning at a community district level does not follow a strategy of minimising damage potential. We find that the dis-

Table 4.7: RSA results: analysis of property values and damages.

Sector	Total property value million DM	%	Property values at risk from flooding (damage potentials) million DM	%	Damage according to flooding scenario +1.5m a.s.1	%
Farmland	1195	7.6	1106	8.3	46	2.4
Live-stock	166	1.1	151	1.1	74	3.9
Productive capital stock, housing excluded	7833	49.9	6514	49.1	748	38.9
Agriculture*	431	2.8	394	3.0	84	4.4
Industries*	2728	17.4	2304	17.4	358	18.6
Commerce and services*	1083	6.9	974	27.3	39	2.0
Transportation, infrastructure, communication*	3591	22.9	2842	21.4	267	13.9
Value of stocks	627	4.0	521	3.9	295	15.4
Housing, inventory included	5566	35.5	4715	35.6	710	36.9
Motor vehicles	304	1.0	258	2.0	50	2.6
Total	15691	100	13265	100	1924	100

* = Included in productive capital stock, housing excluded. Excluded from total.

tribution of damage between the different sectors and its comparison with that of the values at risk gives a first insight into the susceptibility of each sector to flooding, which is again valuable information for improving land use development policies.

The damage figures also demonstrate the importance of this information. The damage of DM 2 billion corresponds with eighteen annual budgets of the district council or one-third of the investments between 1962 and 1990 in coastal defence and flood protection measures in Germany. As can be seen, detailed analysis of the very different vulnerability of flooding within the results is valuable information for strategic development, especially for balancing the design standard for defence structures and the degree of land use restrictions. All in all, the results show that the approach developed so far works well and is able to produce results which are easy to understand: an important objective. Moreover, the test has proved the RSA model to be a functioning tool, and the next development stage will be focused on integrating the RSA model with a GIS, especially in order to produce more detailed results at a local level.

Flood protection priorities and regional development strategies
The application of the RSA gives information for setting flood protection priorities and identifying regional development strategies which is aimed at an integrative and future-orientated solution.

A spatial distribution of damage potentials shows the areas of major concern: the so-called 'hot spots'. Hot spot analysis, in combination with the analysis of the reasons for and causes of such high damage potential, makes the decision makers aware that in many cases the reason for high damage potential is inadequate perception of risk on behalf of the owners, and inadequate land use planning which does not take into account the criteria of risk minimisation on behalf of the institutions responsible for land use planning at the community level.

The importance of land use strategies, then, is particularly apparent since the trend is towards growing disenchantment with structural solutions to flood problems on environmental grounds. In order to develop new land use strategies, the model application can assist by comparing total damage potential within an existing scheme area with the maximum acceptable risk, thus using a decision rule similar to those used in the insurance industry. A non-tolerable overall risk can lead, for example, to the partitioning of protection devices so as to protect smaller areas, or other strategies; this is akin to managed retreat. The results in the case study suggest that such strategies are necessary, and provide information for the required public agencies.

Regional Scale Analysis: conclusions and some policy implications
We have two findings from our analysis at a regional scale which could help develop best practice for protecting flood plain regions. They refer to the time horizon for redeveloping regions and the holistic approach for getting optimised results. With regard to the time horizon, RSA dictates a long time horizon, and our RSA model provides the overview necessary for this. It also can be an input to holistic decision making, whereby flood damage potential information is integrated with other quantified and semi-quantified variables, each of which could affect decisions as to flood mitigation strategies.

In addition, we have seen that our RSA model has proved to be worthwhile and applicable to solving questions involved in the sustainable development of flood plain areas and coastal zones. Given the need to incorporate problems such as sea-level rise, climatic oscillations and other major considerations, the RSA is appropriate, or at least more appropriate than micro-economic analysis.

In addition, the feasibility of obtaining data for the RSA has been proved, at least in Germany, and other applications elsewhere will follow. This, then, will lead to the development of a computerised decision support system to facilitate flood plain management and coastal plain management in different European regions. To this end, it is important to build interfaces into the RSA software packages to existing official data sources, particularly concerned with property values. By way of output, it is important to interface the RSA system with GIS, allowing such devices to give good descriptions of different flood scenarios and damage potential, thus aiding decision support.

In addition, our experience has shown that damage potentials within flood-prone areas can be analysed without major methodological problems. Future planning of coastal zone areas and river flood control systems should be based on priority setting, founded on 'hot spots' analysis, within a regional land use planning context. Such information is seen as a basic requirement, serving both technical design and economic and social planning. It aims to answer questions such as what are the benefits and costs of flood alleviation; what distributional effects will result and how should these be tackled; which parts of the regions and which groups in the population are the winners and which are the losers; what is the optimal development strategy for the region analysed, and what is the compromise between resource allocation efficiency and distributional aspects.

Our RSA model also generates results which can be used to create a variety of indicators showing specific figures per capita, per employee and so on. This enables us to display and analyse the particular conditions in the regions concerned, and to compare them with neighbouring regions. Moreover, it enables us to discuss and analyse whether the region under consideration is able to cope with the problem at hand from its own resources. From such results it becomes possible to discuss the necessary resource redistribution on a rational basis, and to decide on actual grant allocations. The application of RSA for all regions affected by major flooding problems would give transparency about resource needs, and therefore a basis for developing best practice in priority setting and budget allocation.

ASSESSMENT

This chapter has reviewed the needs for a hierarchical decision-making system, and data and models to correspond with this. It has also looked at early trials of RSA, developed in the United Kingdom, and more sophisticated work undertaken in Germany.

The conclusions from this review are that any RSA is quite problematic because it involves a compromise between data availability and output accuracy. We saw this first in the BOCDAM analysis, where very limited data inputs resulted in quite unsophisticated outputs which were nevertheless useful as indicating the order of magnitude of flood problems in different areas. In the German case, a compromise had to be struck between the availability of secondary source data at a local level (for the *Fluren*), and the need for local accuracy given the highly specific flood problems in the case study involved but also the need to link the results to regional planning at a broad scale rather than just local project appraisal. These compromises led to the development of a system which involved some local detail, but retained the adherence to the objective of creating a regional scale overview analysis.

Clearly further work will be necessary on the regional scale. This is because this is the inherent European scale of analysis, as discussed in

Chapter 1, and it does require sophisticated models. However, the sophistication is not in the level of detail covered, but in the wisdom of the compromises between detail and appropriateness. There is a danger that we may concentrate too much on detail, and miss the fact that the RSA must give us data on orders of magnitude of flood vulnerability, rather than absolute accuracy. We can follow the RSA with more detailed investigations, but if we miss the regional scale we may be forced to do more local studies than is wise or than we have resources for.

References

Beyene, M. (1992) *Ein Informationssystem für die Abschätzung von Hochwasserschadens potentialen* (An Information System for the Estimation of Flood Damage Potentials). Aachen, Germany: Mitteilungen Heft 83 des Instituts für Wasserbau und Wasserwirtschaft der Rheinisch-Westfälischen Technischen Hochschule

Bialas, W.F. and Loucks, D.P. (1978) Nonstructural Flood Plain Planning. *Water Resources Research*, 14 (1), 67–74

Chatterton, J.B. and Penning-Rowsell, E.C. (1981) Computer Modelling of Flood Alleviation Benefits. *Proceedings of the American Society of Civil Engineers*, 107 (WR2), 533–47

Council of the European Communities (1992) Council Resolution of 25 February 1992 on the Future Community Policy Concerning the European Coastal Zone (92 /C 59/01). *Official Journal of the European Communities*, C 59/1, 6 March

Delft Hydraulics (1992) *Analysis of Vulnerability to the Impacts of Sea Level Rise. A Case Study for the Netherlands.* Delft, Netherlands: Delft Hydraulics

Delft Hydraulics and Rijkswaterstaat (1991) *Impact of Sea Level Rise on Society. A Case Study for the Netherlands.* Delft, Netherlands: Delft Hydraulics and Rijkswaterstaat

Deutscher Verband für Wasserwirtschaft und Kulturbau (1985) *Ökonomische Bewertung von Hochwasserschutzwirkungen* (Economic assessment of flood mitigating effects). Bonn, Germany: DVWK-Mitteilungen Heft 10

El-Jabi, N. and Ronselle, J. (1987) A Flood Damage Model for Flood Plain Studies. *Water Research Bulletin*, 23 (2), 179–87

Green, C.H.; N'Jai, A. and Neal, J. (1987) *Thames Overview pre-feasibility study. Report to Thames Water Authority.* London, UK: Middlesex University, Flood Hazard Research Centre

Green, C.H. and Penning-Rowsell, E.C. (1985) Evaluating the Intangible Benefits and Costs of a Flood Alleviation Proposal. *Journal of the Institute of Water Engineers and Scientists*, 40 (3), 229–48

Günther, W. and Niekamp, O. (1989) *HOWAS – Hochwasserschadensdaten-Datenverwaltung und Auswertung* (HOWAS – Flood Damage Data – Data Handling and Processing). Beitragssammlung zum 2. Aachen, Germany: Fortbildungslehrgang Wasserwirtschaft des DVWK

Günther, W. and Schmidtke, R.F. (1988) Hochwasserschadensanalysen – Pilot-untersuchung über das Inn-Hochwasser im August 1985 (Flood Damage Analyses – Pilot Investigation on the River Inn Flood in August 1985). *Wasserwirtschaft*, 78(2), 61–8

IPCC (1992) *Global Climate Change and the Rising Challenge of the Sea*. Response Strategies Working Group. Coastal Zone Management Subgroup

Klaus, J. (ed.) (1984) *Entscheidungshilfen für die Infrastrukturplanung (Decision Support System for Assessing Technical Infrastructure)*. Baden-Baden, Germany: Nomos Verlag

Klaus, J.; Lindstadt, H.-J. and Pflügner, W. (1981) *Bewertung wasserwirtschaftlicher Infrastruktur* (Assessment of Water Resources Infrastructure). Germany: Münster-Hiltrup

Klaus, J. and Schmidtke, R.F. (1990) *Bewertungsgutachten für Deichbauvorhaben an der Festlandsküste* (Investment Appraisal for Coastal Flood Defence Schemes). Bonn, Germany: Der Bundesminister für Ernährung, Landwirtschaft und Forsten

Loucks, D.P. (1992) Water Resources Systems Models: their role in planning. *Journal of Water Resources Planning and Management*, 118 (3), 214–23

Ministry of Agriculture, Fisheries and Food (1993) *Flood and Coastal Defence Project Appraisal Guidance Note*. London, UK: Ministry of Agriculture, Fisheries and Food

Parker, D.J.; Green, C.H. and Thompson, P.M. (1987) *Urban Flood Protection Benefits: a project appraisal guide (The Red Manual)*. Aldershot, UK: Gower Technical Press

Penning-Rowsell, E.C. and Chatterton, J.B. (1977) *The Benefits of Flood Alleviation: a manual of assessment techniques (The Blue Manual)*. Aldershot, UK: Gower Technical Press

Penning-Rowsell, E.C.; Chatterton, J.B.; Day, H.J.; Ford, D.T.; Greenaway, M.A.; Smith, D. I.; Wood, T.R. and Witts, R.W. (1987) Comparative Aspects of Computerized Flood Plain Data Management. *Journal of Water Resources Planning and Management*, 113 (6), 725–44

Pflügner, W. (1988) *Nutzenanalysen im Umweltschutz – Der ökonomische Wert von Wasser und Luft (Benefit Analyses in Environmental Protection – The Economic Value of Water and Air)*. Göttingen, Germany: Vanden Hoeck and Ruprecht

Plazak, D.J. (1986) Flood Control Benefits Revisited. *Journal of Water Resources Planning and Management*, 112 (2), 265–76

Schmidtke, R.F. (1993) Estimation of Flood Damage Potentials as Planning Information for Coast Protection Sea Defence Schemes. *Proceedings of the International UNESCO Workshop 'Sea Level Changes and their Consequences for Hydrology and Water Management'*. Nordwijkerhout, Netherlands. Session IC: Socio-economic Impacts, 75–88. Koblenz, Germany: IHP/OHP National Committee of Germany

Suleman, M.; N'Jai, A.; Green, C.H. and Penning-Rowsell, E.C. (1988) *Potential Flood Damage: a major update*. London, UK: Middlesex University, Flood Hazard Research Centre

Torterotot, J.P. (1993) *Le coût des dommages dus aux inondations: estimation et analyse des incertitudes* (The cost of damage due to flooding: assessment and uncertainty analysis). Doctoral thesis. Paris, France: Ecole Nationale des Ponts et Chaussées

Van der Veen, A. and Wierstra, E. (1993). Full Flood Impacts Decision Support

Methods. In EUROflood Project, *First Annual Report*, 45–67. London, UK: Middlesex University

World Coast Conference Organizing Committee (1993) *How to Account for Impacts. Concepts and Tools.* The Hague, Netherlands: World Coast Conference Organizing Committee

CHAPTER 5

Hazard Appraisal: Modelling Sea-level Rise and Safety Standards

Bart Peerbolte

THE CONTEXT

The concept of safety is central to hazard management, embracing as it does concepts of threat and vulnerability. Safety implies foresight, awareness and contingency planning. The lack of safety threatens our lives, our livelihoods and our assets. In flood hazard terms our safety is threatened in all flood plain areas and coastal zones, and nowhere more so than in coastal zones that have a degree of protection but which face greater threats. For in many places in the world the coastal zone represents a focal point for socio-economic development. This often brings about the need for an adequate system of flood alleviation infrastructure to provide sufficient security for the users of the coastal zone against storm surges and consequent erosion and flooding. This infrastructure is likely to include civil engineering works such as embankments, sea dikes, barrier dams, beach walls and storm surge gate barriers.

We need to understand the forces at work and the assets at risk. Two important aspects at the design stage of a flood defence structure are the hydraulic forcing on the structure (water levels, waves and currents) and the value of the assets to be protected. A complication can be that the hydraulic forcing and the values to be protected will change over time: the first, for example, due to sea-level rise; the latter, for example, due to economic development.

A further complication is that the existence of a flood protection system will probably enhance the coastal zone, and this may lead to an increase in the number of settlements there and the values to be protected. At a certain stage the flood protection system may need to be adapted in view of these increased values. If this adaptation does not take place, investment decisions in the coastal zone may be based on incorrect views as to the security against flooding. Such a feeling of false security is dangerous and can lead to an increase in hazardousness.

As discussed in Chapter 2, changes in the natural environment may also influence security against flooding. It has become evident that worldwide socio-economic development has caused a significant increase in carbon dioxide build-up in the atmosphere. There is a general understanding that this will increase the 'greenhouse effect', leading to global warming and consequently to climate change (IPCC 1990). One of the most serious consequences of the greenhouse effect is sea-level rise, endangering the coastal zone and its inhabitants. This implies not only a change in mean sea level; high storm surges may consequently become more frequent and serious. Possible changes in the local climate, leading to changes in wind and storm frequencies, may add to this effect.

This is not all. In many places, land subsidence due to glacial rebound or ground water extraction appears as a relative rise of the sea level. The impacts of such a locally induced sea-level rise are in fact similar to the above eustatic sea-level rise, induced by the greenhouse effect.

This chapter tackles the problems that such an increase in sea level will pose for low-lying coastal areas. It focuses primarily on the Netherlands, where this problem is of particular importance; a great deal of the national income is generated at or below sea level. Nevertheless, the ISOS model developed to evaluate safety levels in these circumstances has the potential for wider application.

The problem

The physical background

The Netherlands is a low-lying nation with about one-third of its area below sea level (Figure 5.1). The country has a long flood history, marked by many storm surge floods. The province of Zeeland was badly hit by the last flood disaster in 1953, which caused almost 2,000

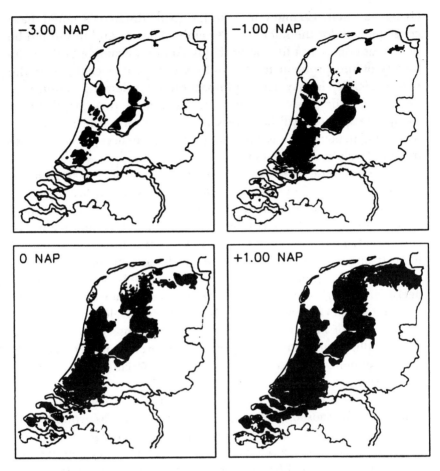

Figure 5.1: The low-lying areas of the Netherlands; after Jelgersma (1992). NAP refers to mean sea level at Amsterdam.

deaths. This disaster triggered a major national effort to upgrade the level of security against flooding in the south-west of the Netherlands, with a project known as the Deltaplan.

The question now is whether, starting from the currently accepted safety levels, substantial policy changes are required in order to be able to cope with sea-level rise in the future. This question is real because sea-level rise will enhance the flood hazard. A complicating factor is that sea-level rise cannot be isolated from other greenhouse effects. If global warming leads to a serious increase in sea-level rise, then the hydrological cycle and thus river discharges are likely to change as well. Changes in extreme peak discharges could have consequences for the safety of river embankments, and this would be of serious concern in the Netherlands. Another example of the complexity of the problem in the Netherlands is that changes in the hydrological cycle may have an impact on water demand (positive or negative) in the low-lying polders. It may well be that adaptation of pumping capacities will be necessary in the future in order to meet increasing demand for discharge to prevent an unacceptable increase in water levels in these polders.

The greenhouse effect is a complex problem which has at least two very characteristic and widely discussed aspects. These are, first, this increase in coastal hazards due to sea-level rise – one of the most serious threats – and, secondly, the uncertainty in predictions of climatic change. This chapter focuses on the increase in coastal hazards and not on the prediction of climate change (which was reviewed in Chapter 2). The overall objective is to contribute to decision making concerning sea-level rise and other climate effects and to this end computational tools have been developed to quantify the impacts of both climate change and response options. A case study application forms our specific objective, namely to quantify the consequences of sea-level rise in the Netherlands and to design proper counter-measures.

As we noted above, additional sea-level rise (through land subsidence) may be caused by local human activities such as ground water extraction. Therefore, the above objectives cover a range of problems wider than 'greenhouse sea-level rise' alone. Thus the methodology and the computational framework we have developed are applicable to the more general problem of flood hazard assessment for low-lying coastal areas, rather than just to the impacts of climate change.

Government policy and standards

The security against flooding and coastal storm surges in the whole of the Netherlands is now codified in a flood protection Act defining fifty-three geographical areas as so-called dike-rings (Government of the Netherlands 1989).

Each area has been allocated a prescribed level of safety defined by its frequency of inundation. Where the inundation frequency cannot be determined, the outside water level frequencies may be adopted as design criteria. The dike-rings are protected by the flood protection system, consisting of sea dikes, dunes, river embankments and flood alleviating structures; they cover the whole of the low-lying part of the nation, which is about 50 per cent of its area (Figure 5.2). The total length of the relevant flood protection systems is about 3,000 km; in contrast the total length of the coastline is only slightly more than 300 km.

Location of dike rings

Legend

—— primary defence structure

—— high grounds

53 number of dike ring

0   20   40   60 km

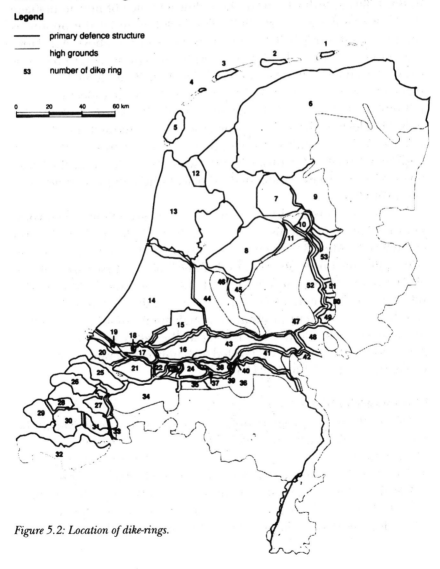

Figure 5.2: Location of dike-rings.

The government policy is to guarantee the level of safety defined in the above law. The tasks of periodic inspection of the primary flood protection system (every five years) and its operation and maintenance are given to local water authorities, partly subsidised by the government (with a 20 per cent grant). In the case of engineering works specifically required to meet the standard security levels, the government contributes 80 per cent of the cost.

As far as the dune coast is concerned, four policies were evaluated in the 1980s in order to make the political choice of how to manage the dunes (Rijkswaterstaat 1989). Fundamental to all the options is the requirement regarding safety laid down in the above Act. However, in places where the dunes are wide enough, whether erosion is to be allowed is still to be considered. The policies evaluated are, first, maintaining the coastline in its present position, irrespective of the interests at stake and, secondly, to take counter-active action – but only in selected places – to protect specific economic or environmental assets. The third policy option is coastal retreat, if the safety requirements allow for this. Fourthly, seaward extension of the coastline at critical places is suggested for places where important interests are involved.

The measures related to the above options predominantly involve sand nourishment but also include 'hard' solutions such as groynes and dams. Figure 5.3 shows the locations along the coast where, in the year 2000, measures are required, following the first three of the above options (Rijkswaterstaat 1989, Louisse and Kuik 1990). In 1990 the Dutch government chose the first option, that is maintaining the coastline in its present position, although some 'natural' movement of the dunes was allowed for as long as the safety standard was not jeopardised. This option was termed 'dynamic preservation' (Ministry of Transport and Public Works 1990).

Our research objectives

In view of the above problem domain and objectives we arrived at the following problem definition: to develop a method by which to evaluate security against flooding and coastal erosion in low-lying coastal areas, with particular reference to a possible increase in sea-level rise.

Based on this problem definition the following research tasks have been formulated. First, we needed to develop a conceptual safety model for the evaluation of flood and erosion hazards in the coastal

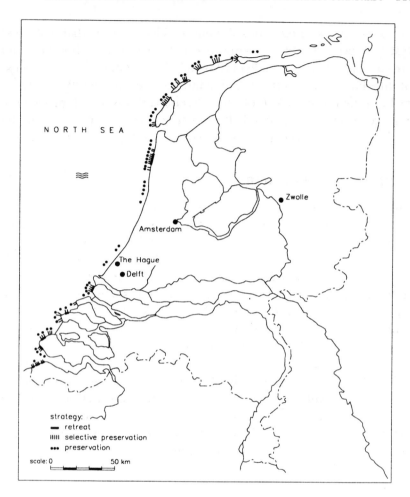

Figure 5.3: Places with erosion measures in the year 2000.

zone. The resulting conceptual safety model serves as a guide to the possible implementation of decision tools for tackling the sea-level rise problems, whereby the emphasis may be either on the physical aspects or on the socio-economic aspects (cf. Figure 1.1). The relevant research task in the Netherlands is to develop a method of analysing the impacts of sea-level rise on the flood protection system in the Netherlands, and to analyse the options available to maintain the established safety levels.

So far, so good. In addition we need to relate the resulting investments in flood protection measures to the values to be protected, in order to assess their worthwhileness. That means that the next research task should concentrate on the impacts of flooding and erosion (i.e. the benefit side of flood alleviation policy). In the context of this chapter, only direct tangible impacts are considered in order to make a first assessment of the benefits of this flood protection. This constraint has defined the research task as evaluating for the Netherlands the direct tangible impacts resulting from sea-level rise.

METHODS AND APPROACHES

The above problem description indicates that we are involved in the inter-relationship between the natural ecosystem and the socio-economic system (Figure 1.1), and that we want to focus on a part of it: that part involved in a rise in sea level. Both systems are important for three reasons specific to this chapter: first, the natural ecosystem transfers sea-level rise to the socio-economic system; secondly, the natural ecosystem may be directly affected by sea-level rise; and, thirdly, human response to sea-level rise may have consequences for the natural ecosystem. This is schematised in Figure 5.4.

There are various indicators that we can use to denote the extent of coastal and dike-related flood hazards, often with varying connotations. Examples are vulnerability to flooding, safety and risk. In order to avoid confusion such concepts need to be defined unambiguously. Figure 5.5 shows the following factors which play a role when analysing the sensitivity and vulnerability of an area to flooding:

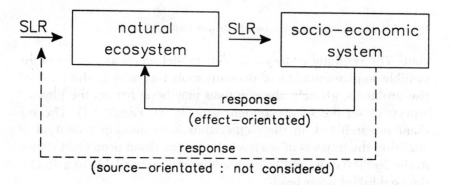

Figure 5.4: The interaction between the socio-economic system and the natural ecosystem.

- Hydraulic forcing (the extent and frequency of wave load, water level, storm surges, cyclones etc.).
- The resistance of the flood defence system to this hydraulic forcing (stability, crest elevation).
- The exposure of features within the vulnerable area, including economic values and other values such as human life, social disruption or environmental damage.
- The susceptibility of the features to flooding and erosion.

These factors reflect more or less the causal relationships and links between the stages in a flood or erosion event. Against the background of this model we have adopted the following specific operational definitions in this research on safety.

1. We define the probability of an extreme event such as a flood or coastal erosion threatening the users of the exposed areas as a hazard.
2. The probability that adverse effects associated with a hazard do not occur is denoted as safety. In general safety is specified in terms of the relevant event and those exposed (for example, the safety of people with regard to coastal flooding).
3. The effects of a hazard on the exposed features are defined as impacts. Physical impacts refer to physical changes to objects due to a hazard; for example, the number of buildings destroyed by a flood, or the parts of a single building which are damaged. Socio-economic impacts represent the valuation of physical impacts, for example, in monetary terms; whereas ecological impacts result from valuation on a specific ecological scale, either ordinal or cardinal. Examples of expressions on a cardinal scale are habitat

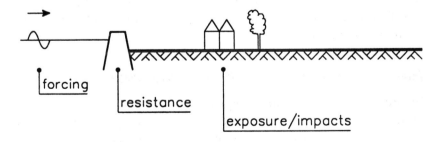

Figure 5.5: Factors in the process of flooding.

loss in square kilometres, primary production in grams of carbon per square kilometre per year, and species diversity in numbers of different species.

4. Vulnerability is defined as a relative impact – that is, relative to the pre-hazard situation. Examples are the fraction of buildings which is destroyed in the case of a flood, or the socio-economic damages with respect to the total value of assets in the relevant area.

5. Risk is defined as the combination of safety and impacts or vulnerability, that is, the combination of a hazard and its consequences, either in an absolute or in a relative sense.

This set of concepts and definitions together is referred to as safety criteria. We recognise there are some differences between aspects of these definitions and those given in Chapter 3.

Based on the different stages in the flooding and erosion process, and the consequential damages and responses, a conceptual safety model has been developed which is shown in Figure 5.6. This diagram is still very schematic and abstract but it provides the framework for making progress. Relevant processes are encapsulated by circles. Examples are the morphological response of the coast to sea-level rise and the growing socio-economic impact due to the interaction between changes in the natural system such as flooding frequencies on the one hand with land use on the other.

Data flows between the processes are indicated by arrows in Figure 5.6. For example, data on flooding frequencies flows to the process determining the socio-economic impact or stress. Information on the different system elements is enclosed by two parallel lines within each box; such information is important in quantifying the different effects. Finally, there are data which are beyond the system, either influencing the system or outputs of the system. Examples of these so-called terminators, indicated by rectangles, are climatic and socio-economic scenarios.

IMPLEMENTATION: STARTING POINTS AND ASSUMPTIONS

In order to define the next steps in implementing the ISOS safety model the following assumptions and starting points have been adopted. First, we focus on the effects of climate change. This means that anthropogenic and natural changes, not caused by climatic change, are not taken into account. An exception is made for land

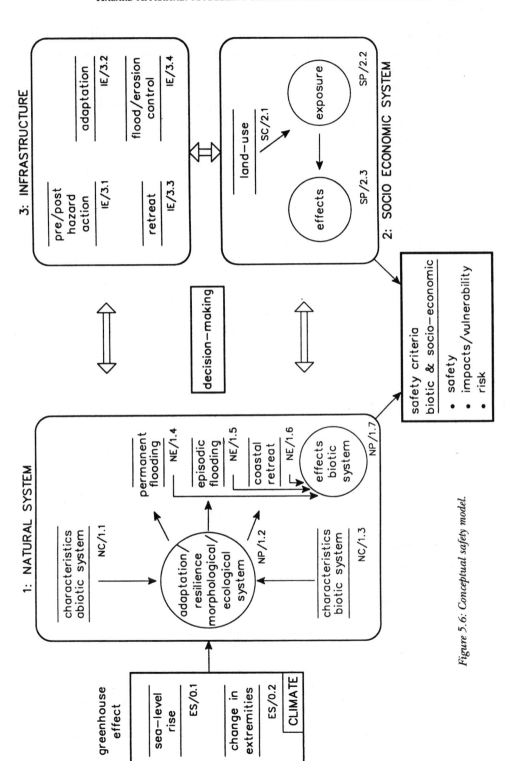

Figure 5.6: Conceptual safety model.

subsidence which may be caused by gas extraction, ground water pumping, or dike construction; or by land reclamation and associated ground water table lowering, which is of special significance in the Netherlands.

Secondly, climate change will be expressed in a pre-defined set of scenario variables, possibly including subsidence effects on the variable relative sea-level rise; the physical mechanism of the greenhouse effect is not modelled. This means that the best available knowledge from existing literature is used to define the climate scenarios to be applied (Chapter 2). Thirdly, we only consider counter-measures which aim to neutralise or alleviate the impacts of climate change, with major emphasis on the problem of ensuring safety against flooding and coastal erosion. The elimination or reduction of climate change itself is not considered. In other words, effect-orientated and not source-orientated policy options are analysed. Finally, we assume that the entire flood protection system in the Netherlands has to meet safety standards as required by the Flood Protection Act (Government of the Netherlands 1989).

On the basis of the above specification and constraints, we can identify more specifically a number of steps to be taken. These encompass the identification of the impacts of sea-level rise and other greenhouse effects on the complete water system, with emphasis on safety against flooding, the identification of the measures available to prevent or reduce negative impacts and the possible side-effects of these, and the comparison of alternative strategies or policy options, each consisting of a set of measures.

THE MODEL'S CONCEPTS AND SPECIFICATIONS

Introduction

The general conceptual safety model shown as Figure 5.6 has been elaborated further in order to assess the impacts of sea-level rise in the Netherlands.

The processes in the three main system elements – the natural system, the socio-economic system and the infrastructure – have only been indicated very generally, and the model is still an abstract model. This means that the data structure, the schematisation of the relevant processes and the topography of the model still have to be defined in detail. Just how detailed is related to the impacts which are to be evaluated. Their required accuracy determines the method and accuracy of implementation of the safety model. Therefore, detailed modelling of all processes which play a possible role should not be attempted *a priori*. In addition, we need to be aware of the required temporal scale of the model; climatic changes evolve very gradually, whereas human responses are implemented in a relatively short period of time. Furthermore, the scenarios and measures which will be evaluated have to be defined.

The elaboration of the safety model

In the first instance changes in the different climate factors result in changes in the water environment, that is the near-shore coastal waters, estuaries and rivers. In addition, low-lying lands will be affected by impacts on the water management system due to changes in precipitation and evaporation and to salinity intrusion. All these changes are responsible for potential impacts on the users of the natural system including virtually all socio-economic activities in the threatened areas. Because the various water environments have their own typical response characteristics, the natural system has been dis-aggregated, resulting in the following sub-systems: Land, Coastal Zone, Coastal Seas and Estuaries, Lower Rivers, Upper Rivers, and Lakes. These are described below.

Land sub-system. This sub-system comprises the land and water systems within the main flood protection system; areas of high elevation border this sub-system on the land side. In the case of the Netherlands, the area covered by dike-rings forms the Land sub-system; these dike-rings are specified in the Flood Protection Act and the landward boundary is defined by the 'high grounds' line.

Coastal Zone sub-system. In the context of sea-level rise, the coastal zone is obviously the area most discussed. In general the width of the coastal zone is not absolutely defined and varies depending on the problem domain. It may on the one hand be governed by geo-graphical, geological and geomorphological criteria. On the other hand, the interests the model's users have in the problem area may dictate their delimitation of the coastal zone. If the coastal zone is delineated as the area influenced by sea-level rise, then virtually the whole of the low-lying part of the Netherlands would be included.

However, following the above definition of the Land sub-system, we define the coastal zone as the seaward border of the Land sub-system, including the foreshore. Its primary function is to protect the land from the sea. A number of functions in the coastal zone itself will also be affected by sea-level rise – such as recreation, nature conservation and fresh ground water storage areas. The coastal zone consists mainly of dunes and sandy beaches; about 10 per cent of the Dutch coastline consists of dikes or other 'hard' structures such as sea dikes, promenades and groynes. Large beach 'plains' also form part of the coastal zone.

Coastal Seas and Estuaries sub-system. The morphology of coastal seas and estuaries is strongly influenced by the mean sea level, the tidal regime, the wave climate and sediment sources and sinks. Such areas are often characterised by high turbidity, a high biological productivity and intensive human activity (for navigation, fisheries, harbour operations and recreation). In estuarine areas and coastal seas we often find tidal wetlands and intertidal areas of significant environmental value.

Lower Rivers sub-system. Sea-level rise will propagate up-river due to backwater effects. Flood protection structures (dikes) along the rivers must therefore be adapted to sea-level rise. The Lower Rivers sub-system includes the lower branches of river systems which are influenced by the tide, and also their flood plains.

Upper Rivers sub-system. This sub-system comprises the branches of rivers in the study area which are not influenced by the tide. The flood plains are included in this sub-system; the boundaries along the rivers are the main flood embankments. Backwater effects may also be felt in the upper rivers, although to a lesser extent than in the lower rivers.

Lakes sub-system. This sub-system comprises large lake systems, which have their own typical response to sea-level rise and related climatic changes. In the case of the Netherlands, Lake IJssel and Lake Marken, fed by the IJssel river, are candidates for this sub-system. The effects of sea-level rise on lakes may include a rise in their water level as the drainage capacity may reduce. This implies consequences for the safety against flooding of the surrounding Land sub-system. Changing river inflow and changes in precipitation and evaporation may have the same type of effect.

In the case of the Netherlands the above set of six sub-systems falls into two categories, namely the 'dry' Land sub-system, which is flood-protected by a system of major flood defences, and the five 'wet' sub-systems (Figure 5.7). In principle there is no distinction between the two; all sub-systems are subject to certain flood frequencies and the division between wet and dry is a matter of definition. The point, however, is that in the case of the Netherlands a publicly defined level of safety is maintained for the users and functions within the Land sub-system.

Specification of the impacts

The criteria we consider in respect of impacts are related to safety against flooding, to investment costs for flood protection measures, and to economic and environmental impacts. These are specified below.

Safety. Safety against flooding is defined as the probability of being protected from a flood. In the model this is operationalised by substituting the average frequency of exceedance of water levels causing a flood.

Investment cost. This impact category represents the cost associated with investments in flood protection infrastructure. We identify the following sub-categories:

- investment costs following from the planning, design, construction and maintenance of physical infrastructure, related to the safety of the sea defence system – including dikes, dunes and other infrastructure works;
- the cost of artificial beach nourishment to safeguard the dune coast or protect user functions in the dune area;
- the cost of adaptation of the main dike system to maintain the required safety level in the protected areas;
- the cost of infrastructure works (pumping stations and discharge sluices) in the barrier dam separating Lake IJssel from the Wadden Sea (the Afsluitdijk);

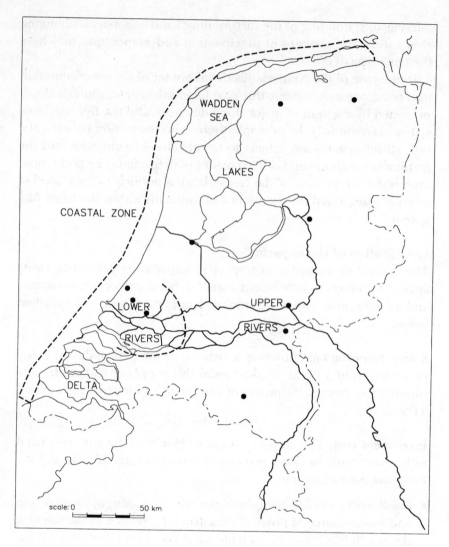

Figure 5.7: Location of natural sub-systems.

- the cost of raising or embanking the port, industrial and residential areas situated outside the main flood protection system and not protected by the above adaptations to the main dike system;
- the cost of adaptations to the water management system – these costs include drainage costs and water supply costs, including those for sprinkler irrigation.

Economic costs. This impact category concerns economic losses resulting from changing hydraulic and hydrological conditions. The sub-categories identified are:

- the economic cost due to drought and salinity damage in the agricultural sector;
- the economic cost due to efficiency losses in electricity production (owing to the adjustment of plant operation due to possible shortage of cooling water in the summer season with reduced river discharges);
- the economic impacts on the flood plains of rivers where the agricultural sector (dairy farming) and industry (brick factories) may face increasing flood frequencies.

Environmental impacts. This category of impacts is related to the natural environment. Although we do not attempt to express impacts on the environment in monetary terms (Chapter 3), a number of pointers in the natural system, induced by sea-level rise, can be used as indicators of the possible impacts on the environment. The sub-categories concerned are the following:

- the loss of dune areas of high environmental value caused by increasing coastal erosion;
- the loss of valuable wetland areas in the estuarine environment owing to sea-level rise;
- the increase in salinity levels of ground water and surface waters caused by saline seepage;
- a fall in ground water levels due to changes in water management practices;
- changes in flooding frequencies of river flood plains with important environmental values;
- the effects on water quality in the fresh and salt water systems (algal blooms and oxygen depletion);
- ecological effects (changes to carbon fluxes and related biomass) in estuarine areas.

Scenario specification

A scenario is defined as a set of exogenous parameters (scenario variables) reflecting uncertain future developments or situations that affect the functioning of the system under study. Rather than being chosen arbitrarily a scenario should comprise a consistent combination of scenario variables; this implicitly includes suppositions concerning relationships between scenario variables. For example, a high temperature rise scenario is probably linked to a high sea-level rise scenario. In fact, the set of scenario variables defines the boundary of our study.

The primary variable in this study is, of course, sea-level rise. In addition some other parameters related to climate change have to be adopted as scenario variables. The major guideline for the selection of these parameters is their potential significance to the natural (water) systems and, ultimately, to the population at large.

Looking at the left side of the system diagram shown in Figure 5.6, we can identify a number of climate factors: wind climate, sea-level rise, hydrological regime and temperature. The wind climate is responsible for the wave climate and storm surge set-up along the coast. The wind climate may change in many respects, such as direction, strength and distribution over time (Chapter 2). Future changes in wind climate cannot be predicted yet, and we therefore simplify this by taking storm surge set-up – that is, a rise in tidal water levels due to storms – as a scenario variable.

In addition to sea-level rise we introduce precipitation, evaporation and river discharge as scenario variables reflecting changes in the hydrological regime. Temperature rise of water is also considered as a scenario variable, because of its impact on the aquatic ecosystems.

Measures to be adopted
A large variety of measures which influence climate change can be considered. The starting point, however, is that measures which aim to influence the greenhouse effect itself are not considered here. In this analysis we deal only with the problem of maintaining safety and define suitable strategies to cope with this problem. The most important category of measures aims to safeguard the dike-rings from increasing flood frequency and includes dike-raising and beach nourishment. However, measures aimed at the protection of activities in the flood prone areas, measures affecting the water management system, and measures to reduce the negative impacts on the environment are also considered.

Data structure

The data structure in the ISOS model is based on the following requirements: that climate scenarios are user defined, that the strategies (i.e. sets of measures phased over time) are also user defined, and that geographical schematisation is derived from the spatial variability of impacts.

For the Land sub-system the dike-ring system of the Netherlands with pre-defined safety standards according to the Flood Protection Act serves as a basis for the geographical schematisation. Outside the primary flood protection system the spatial variability of the effects of climate change will form a basis for schematisation there. A requirement of the model is also that the time scale is in accordance with rates of change of climate parameters and related impacts, and with the phasing and implementation time of counter-measures.

The primary flood embankments, dunes and other flood protection structures form a system of closed cells, each with a specified safety standard. These cells are defined as dike-rings and form the basis of the geographical schematisation. At the boundary of the low-lying part of the Netherlands the dike-rings border on areas with higher elevation which do not need protection against flooding. Such areas are marked by a 'high ground line'.

Thus two types of area beyond the dike-rings can be distinguished: namely, water areas or low-lying, flood-prone areas; and the zones of higher elevation, which do not need to be protected from flooding. The national border forms the ultimate boundary of the geographical schematisation.

The low-lying areas or water surfaces outside the dike-rings are subdivided into basic areas which are uniform in terms of hydraulic parameters expressing the most important effects of the applied climatic changes on the given area. These parameters, amongst other things, determine the safety of adjacent dike-rings, or the flooding frequency of flood-prone areas. These areas will be referred to as hydraulic impact areas (HIA). Thus each HIA embodies a set of values translating the effect of the climate scenario variables into actual values for the given area. A further schematisation is that an HIA, if it borders and affects a dike-ring, affects this dike-ring as a whole.

Within dike-rings, HIA and high ground areas it is in principle possible to discriminate within these units according to functionality, say (function) cells. In the present case, this option is only used for the HIA. The principle of all this spatial schematisation is depicted in Figure 5.8.

Final implementation

The final implementation of the ISOS model is based on the principles outlined above and on the information on the different sub-systems; the land side of the model is based on the system of dike-rings. The number of dike-rings included in the model amounts to seventy-one, consisting of fifty-three dike-rings following the Flood Protection Act, four dike-rings enclosing areas of undefined safety level and, finally, fourteen hypothetical dike-rings, consisting of dams separating HIA.

Dike-ring sets of the same safety standard which are adjacent to each other are grouped into dike-ring clusters; the ISOS modelling of the Netherlands comprises fourteen dike-ring clusters. In addition, one cluster comprises dike-rings which have no official safety standard (at the time of the implementation of the ISOS model). These dike-rings are minor areas, 'forgotten' in the schematisation according to the Flood Protection Act. Furthermore, the higher part of the country is sub-divided into three parts which also form clusters: the eastern part of the country, the Veluwe (the central part) and Brabant/Limburg (the southern part). Finally, four clusters consist of

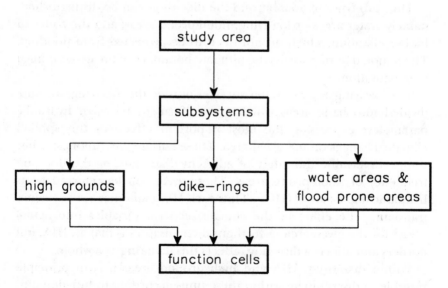

Figure 5.8: Principle of spatial schematisation.

dams separating different HIA. The compilation of all dike-ring clusters, together with areas at a higher elevation, constitutes the Land sub-system.

The schematisation of the 'water' side of the model is based on HIA, which are sub-divisions of the sub-systems (excluding the Land sub-system, which represents the areas enclosed by the dikes). The identity of these 'water' sub-systems is based on natural and geographical characteristics. They embody spatially distributed sets of uniform hydraulic parameters, defined as HIA.

APPLICATION AND RESULTS

With the ISOS model as described, we can now analyse the options available to maintain the established safety levels. By analysing the impacts for different combinations of climate scenarios and matching strategies – that is, strategies which yield the lowest cost of dike-raising without violating the safety standards set in the Flood Protection Act – the best set of options can be determined (Peerbolte *et al.* 1991).

The cost of dike-raising strategies

Depending on the climate scenario which emerges, the cost of dike-raising to maintain the established levels of safety will range from 2,600 million Dutch guilders to 17,500 million Dutch guilders. The first figure will match a rise in sea level of 0.2 m; the latter a very unfavourable scenario of climate change, namely a rise in sea level of 0.85 m combined with a significant increase in storm surges (0.65 m). Figure 5.9 shows the total cumulative costs of dike-raising (excluding the Lakes sub-system) in order to cope with 0.2 m, 0.6 m and 1.0 m sea-level rises, and the above unfavourable scenario (UNF.ALL).

Responding with measures to the most unfavourable scenario which has been analysed will probably create an unnecessarily high level of safety because such an unfavourable scenario is not very likely to occur. We therefore do not recommended starting to implement the corresponding dike-raising measures now.

Detailed analysis, however, indicates that a strategy for coping with a 0.6 m or 1.0 m sea-level rise alone (without changes in storm surges and waves) does not lead to dike-raising in the next five years. If at that time a 0.6 m rise in sea level is the most realistic scenario, no dike-raising is necessary for another period of five years. If, on the

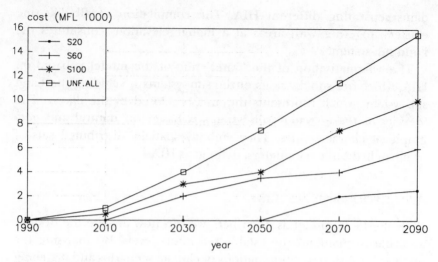

Figure 5.9: Cumulative cost of dike-raising for different scenarios.

other hand, the 1.0 m sea-level rise scenario develops, temporary 'unsafety' has to be accepted in, at most, nineteen dike-rings. That means that in nineteen dike-rings the safety standards cannot be met all the time, unless the height of dike-raising is adapted. No detailed analysis has been carried out to quantify such adaptations. Unsafety is defined here as the ratio of the actual and standard flood frequency (safety standard). Practically, an unsafety of 1.2 means that the actual flood return period is a factor of 1.2 smaller than the standard return period.

If a strategy is implemented matching a rise of 1.0 m in sea level, some 440 million Dutch guilders will have to be invested in dike-raising projects in the second five years in order to guarantee the required safety levels. However, in view of the controversy about such sea-level scenarios, it does not seem justifiable now to advocate a strategy matching a sea-level rise of 1.0 m.

Considering scenarios of 0.6 m and 0.2 m sea-level rise, the analysis has shown that a strategy matching a 0.2 m sea-level rise will lead to a relatively small degree of unsafety after thirty-five to forty years if a rise of 0.6 m develops. However, it is not certain that this scenario will occur; whilst a sea-level rise of about 0.6 m in one hundred years was considered earlier as the most likely scenario (IPCC 1990), more recent publications are more conservative (IPCC 1992, Wigley and Raper 1992).

If the dike-raising strategy is aimed at maintaining safety standards with a sea-level rise scenario of 0.2 m while a sea-level rise of 0.6 m develops, after forty to fifty years a reconsideration of the strategy may be justified because of structural unsafety. The limited unsafety after thirty to forty years will probably be neutralised when adapting the dike-raising strategy under conditions of structural unsafety at a later stage. Taking into account an implementation time of roughly twenty years, there still remain twenty to thirty years in which to arrive at more firm conclusions about responses to this future sea-level rise.

In conclusion, therefore, it does not seem to be justified to deviate from a conservative strategy at this time. In Figure 5.10 the maximum unsafety in the Netherlands is shown for strategies matching a 0.2 m (conservative strategy) and a 0.6 m sea-level rise (anticipating strategy), where a scenario of 0.6 m develops.

In policy terms, however, the operation of the storm surge barriers is another matter. If the frequency of storm surges increases as a result of sea-level rise, the closing frequency of the storm surge gate barrier in the Eastern Scheldt will increase correspondingly. There is therefore no reason to raise the dikes surrounding the Eastern Scheldt. In the (theoretical) case that the operation of the barrier is not adapted to climatic change, the dikes along the Eastern Scheldt will need to

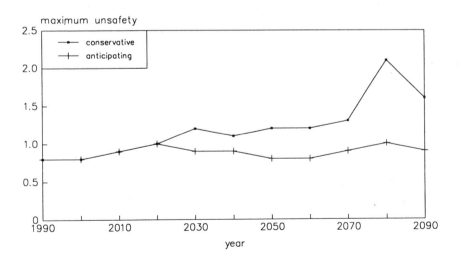

Figure 5.10: Maximum unsafety in the Netherlands with a 0.6 m rise in sea level, for a conservative strategy anticipating dike-raising.

be raised in accordance with the rising sea level. Such a theoretical comparison between the two situations illustrates the saving on dike-raising costs which are made by operating the barrier. It appears from the ISOS model that the savings on dike-raising around the Eastern Scheldt would amount to about 1,000 million Dutch guilders at a sea-level rise of 0.6 m per century. In these computations it has been assumed that the sea bed adapts to sea-level rise by sedimentation to an extent of 80 per cent of the sea-level rise.

The same type of comparison can be made for the storm surge barrier in the Rotterdam Waterway which is at present under construction. This barrier will only be closed under extreme conditions because shipping should not be disrupted. That means that the design water levels in areas behind the structure will reduce and the associated saving on dike-raising in these areas is large and amounts to about 2,400 million Dutch guilders.

In parallel to the Eastern Scheldt surge barrier, the closing frequency of the Rotterdam barrier will also need to match a possible increase in the frequency of storm surges due to sea-level rise. This leads to another saving on dike-raising cost in areas directly landward of the barrier, to the extent of 275 million Dutch guilders over the next one hundred years, at a sea-level rise of 0.6 m.

The other impacts concerning coastal (dune) protection, water management and assets in flood-prone areas outside the dike-rings appear to be, as far as the cost is concerned, significantly lower than the cost of dike-raising, with the exception of adapting flood-prone areas. Raising of industrial sites and quay walls in harbours and so on lead, in the case of a sea-level rise of 0.6 m per century, to an additional cost which is about 20 per cent of the cost of maintaining the required level of safety in the dike-rings. The expected increase in pumping cost associated with water management is estimated to be 7 per cent of the cost of maintaining that level of safety.

Considering the tangible economic values protected by the flood defence system, we conclude that the capital value of any increased potential flood damages far exceeds the investments needed to upgrade the system. The term 'damage consensus' factor is used here, to incorporate our assessment of the reliability of potential flood damage data. Given a sea-level rise between 0.3 and 1.0 m per 100 years, investment in dike-raising of only 0.04% to 1.25% of the potential damage at stake is sufficient to maintain the present safety level:

the 'damage consensus' factor is 0.04 to 1.25. These figures derive from runs of the ISOS model and a vulnerability model which computes the values at risk. Obviously as the damage consensus factor approaches 100, the completeness and reliability of the flood damage data built into the vulnerability model is more crucial. We see here, however, that given the assumptions we made regarding the discount rate (5 to 9 per cent), the capital growth factor (2 per cent) and the damage factor (10 to 40 per cent), the cost of dike-raising to match the sea-level rise scenarios of 0.3 m, 0.6 m and 1.0 m is probably much less than the benefits to be obtained. However, known flood damage data show a rather large scatter. The consequence is that the benefits of flood alleviation cannot be determined with an accuracy which is sufficient to allow the detailed design of flood protection works.

SOME POLICY IMPLICATIONS

In a number of countries, such as the United States and the United Kingdom, the design philosophy of flood alleviation schemes is based on benefit-cost analysis (BCA); this implies that the optimal design is obtained when the level of investment in flood alleviation plus the remaining damages counter-balance the avoided damages.

In the Netherlands, regionally differentiated standards of flood safety have been introduced based on observed extreme storm surge levels on the one hand and economic considerations on the other. The choice of safety standards is here, however, a political choice. Although BCA may provide useful information to support the design of small- and medium-scale flood defence systems, for large-scale problems the establishment of safety standards can be more desirable, whereby the non-qualifiable values protected play, amongst other things, an important role.

The practice of BCA in flood alleviation policies also has some well-known controversial facets. Discounting future values (benefits and costs), to mention one, leads to disregarding future damages due to sea-level rise which reveal themselves gradually over the very long term. This results, in turn, in investments that are inadequate to counteract these future sea-level rise impacts. Without presenting a solution to this problem, in the research described in this chapter the time streams of costs and benefits have been presented without discounting to present values. We believe in this way, on a policy level and for this case, that the information on benefits and costs is presented in a way that is as clear and as objective as possible.

Another well-known aspect of BCA is the need to express benefits and costs in a single measure, preferably on a monetary scale. Because flood impacts include an important intangible component, techniques are required to value these components. In the Netherlands this aspect of flood safety, although often mentioned, has not often been a topic of fundamental research and it deserves more attention. Furthermore, it appears from other studies that indirect flood impacts (which may be both tangible and intangible) are often substantial and should not be ignored.

The starting point of this case study was the definition of safety given in the new Flood Protection Act. Here, safety is defined as the inundation frequency of the dike-rings or, as a substitute if this cannot be determined exactly, the exceedance frequency of design conditions (that is, the water levels and wave heights) of the main flood protection structures surrounding the dike-rings: dikes, dunes, gate barriers and sluices. In this study the latter interpretation is applied.

Based on the ISOS model, the main conclusion regarding dike-raising is that there is no reason now to anticipate more severe scenarios than the 0.2 m sea-level rise. With this scenario an average additional cost of approximately 60 million Dutch guilders per year may be expected after about sixty years from now. It seems it will be justified to reconsider this dike-raising strategy after thirty to forty years, and to intensify dike-raising if the data then point to a higher rate of sea-level rise. If, within this period of time, a more serious scenario is seen to be inevitable, there is still time to switch to a dike-raising strategy matching these new predictions. This conclusion is based on the computed unsafety and dike-raising costs, and their sensitivity for a number of sea-level rise scenarios.

The above considerations do not detract from the need continuously to maintain the current flood protection system in order to meet the present safety standards. This also holds for the sandy coast where, according to the current policy, artificial sand nourishment is applied to minimise erosion and to preserve the current coastline. The costs of this maintenance and protection of the sandy coast are low compared with the adaptation cost of the whole flood protection system.

As described above, the design of a flood alleviation system or establishing safety standards is, in some way, based on costs and benefits, but flood damages show high variance. Therefore it is recommended that policy makers might express the benefits of a flood alleviation system in terms of values at stake and establish a damage 'consensus' factor in order to determine the desired investments. Undoubtedly numerous criteria will play a role in the choice of such a factor.

Be that as it may, the increase in potential flood damages in the economically most important dike-rings in the Netherlands induced by sea-level rise exceeds the cost of dike-raising which would be necessary to fulfil the present safety standards. For sea-level rise scenarios of 0.6 m and 1.0 m, the expected damages are orders of magnitude higher than the cost of dike-raising to prevent such damages. If such scenarios were ever to occur, adaptation of the flood protection system is certainly the most feasible solution, even when considering only direct tangible flood impacts.

It is expected, but not evaluated in this study, that adaptations to the flood protection system in order to take due account of values other than direct tangible effects – such as bequest and existence values attached to flood plain landscapes – will not significantly influence this low ratio of costs versus benefits. Whether or not such additional investments are made is a political choice because such values cannot be put directly on the same monetary scale.

There are still important uncertainties in all critical stages of our analysis, independent of the uncertainties surrounding climate change itself. These are the effects of climate change on the required adaptation of the dikes; the cost of such adaptations; the changes in flooding frequencies resulting from climate change; and the features at risk, their values and susceptibility to flooding. However, such uncertainties are not crucial to our results. In other words, further model refinement will, in the case of the Netherlands, not lead to a different conclusion. The refinement of individual analysis steps remains feasible, in order to optimise the chosen solution in the design phase of flood defence measures; for example, better hydraulic and morphological models could enable better prediction of the influence of climate change on the required adaptations of the flood protection system. This will be true as long as the reduction in total cost exceeds the cost of such refinement.

In addition to the above conclusions about the implementation of the model to the Netherlands, the study has produced a blueprint for sea-level rise impact assessment which can be applied in any other case. This generic facility can be used as a framework, in which the various modules can be adapted to any new area under consideration.

REFERENCES

Government of the Netherlands (1989) *Algemene regels ter verzekering van de beveiliging door waterkeringen tegen overstromingen door het buitenwater en regeling van enkele daarmee verband houdende aangelegenheden* (Wet op de Waterkering) (Dutch Flood Protection Act). Tweede Kamer der Staten-Generaal. Vergaderjaar 1988–9, 21 195, nos 1–2. SDU Uitgeverij. The Hague, Netherlands

IPCC (1990) *Climate Change, the IPCC Scientific Assessment. Intergovernmental Panel on Climate Change* (Houghton, J.T.; Jenkins, G.J. and Ephraums, J.J., eds). Cambridge, UK: Cambridge University Press

IPCC (1992) *Climate Change 1992 – the Supplementary Report to the IPCC Scientific Assessment. Intergovernmental Panel on Climate Change* (Houghton, J.T.; Callander, B.A. and Varney, S.K., eds). World Meteorological Organization/United Nations Environment Programme. Cambridge, UK: Cambridge University Press

Jelgersma, S. (1992) Vulnerability of the Coastal Lowlands of the Netherlands to a Future Sea-level Rise. In Tooley, M.J. and Jelgersma, S. (eds), *Impacts of Sea-level Rise on European Coastal Lowlands.* The Institute of British Geographers. Oxford, UK: Blackwell Publishers

Louisse, C.J. and Kuik, A.J. (1990) Coastal Defence Alternatives in The Netherlands. In: *The Dutch Coast* (Report of a session of the 22nd International Conference on Coastal Engineering 1990). Ministry of Transport and Public Works/Rijkswaterstaat. Delft, The Netherlands: Delft Hydraulics

Ministry of Transport and Public Works (1990) *A New Coastal Defence Policy for the Netherlands.* The Hague, Netherlands: Ministry of Transport and Public Works

Peerbolte, E.B.; Baarse, G.; Ronde, J.G. de and Vrees, L. de (1991) *Impact of Sea level Rise on Society, a case study for the Netherlands.* Final Report, H750. Netherlands: Rijkswaterstaat and Delft Hydraulics

Rijkswaterstaat (1989) *Kustverdediging na 1990. Discussienota.* The Hague, Netherlands: Ministry of Transport and Public Works

Wigley, T.M.L. and Raper, S.C.B. (1992) Implications for Climate and Sea Level of Revised IPCC Emissions Scenarios. *Nature,* 357, 28 May

CHAPTER 6

Real-time Hazard Management: Flood Forecasting, Warning and Response

Dennis Parker, Maureen Fordham and Jean-Philippe Torterotot

INTRODUCTION

In previous chapters in this volume we have been concerned primarily with assessing the nature of flood hazards, and the threats that they pose to vulnerable populations. Only in Chapter 5, on safety standards and the need for dike-raising in the Netherlands, have we considered responses to the hazard based on that analysis. Dike-raising, moreover, is fundamentally a structural solution to flood hazard problems – necessitating as it does carefully designed engineering works to counter the threat of flooding from the North Sea, bearing in mind the problems caused by precipitation within dike-rings and flood emanating from rivers flowing into the areas concerned.

We turn our attention now to one type of non-structural measure (Figure 1.2), concerned with providing information to potential flood victims on the basis of which they can react with flood-mitigating actions. In addition, such forecasting and warning systems generally have an element which gives advice to those potentially suffering from flooding, in the form of what actions they should take to minimise losses.

In this respect, we see that dependence is growing upon flood forecasting, warning and response systems (FFWRS) for managing flood hazards within the European Union, as elsewhere. A number of factors are responsible. Flood forecasting has improved with enhanced hydrometric and telemetric data collection networks, with the spread of weather radar and with the use of electronic data analysis and numerical forecasting.

In addition, increased economic activity and population growth and/or redistribution has intensified flood plain use and rising flood loss potential is the consequence. There is also growing recognition amongst the public, environmental pressure groups and engineers of the adverse environmental impacts of some structural flood control measures. Therefore alternative non-structural measures are being employed, especially FFWRS. For example, FFWRS are critical for communities along the River Maas. The Dutch have a strong ethos of preserving natural river environments. Communities on the Maas prefer to live with the flood hazard rather than modify channels and flood plains, and this helps preserve the intrinsic character of their villages.

On occasions, also, structural solutions to flood hazards are technically or economically infeasible and therefore reliance is placed on FFWRS. Where flood dikes or embankments are used, these only provide protection to a given standard. In protected flood zones development may be extensive and vulnerable to dike breaching or overtopping so that complementary FFWRS are necessary. Lastly, a frequent reason for high losses in flood disasters is either the lack of a FFWRS or inadequate FFWRS. Demands are often made for new or improved FFWRS in the post-disaster phase.

Flood forecasting, warning and response systems have therefore become an important means of modifying the vulnerability of communities to flood hazards in both unprotected areas and protected zones with residual flood risks. Within this context the research for this chapter has been divided into four components. First, we have concentrated on the development of a generic model identifying components of the FFWRS. Secondly, we have made comparisons of alternative system components adopted across the European Union. Thirdly, the reanalysis of existing data on flood warning dissemination and response has provided fresh insights; and, fourthly, we have selected additional case studies to provide more detail with which to commence model calibration.

Within this research attention is focused principally upon the links between forecasting, warning and response, and upon warning dissemination processes and response mechanisms. Whilst flood forecasting methodologies, techniques and achievements are an important starting point, our research focus is not principally upon the technical aspects of flood forecasting as such, which are well covered elsewhere (Saul 1992). In a European context one of the most important variables influencing the adoption and success of FFWRS is the rate of response of run-off and river levels to precipitation, and the time available to issue and disseminate flood warnings and to respond. Our research therefore includes FFWRS for both flash floods and floods with a slow rate of rise.

OUR RESEARCH QUESTIONS

Conceptual questions and guides
One of the principal objectives of our research has been to assess the usefulness of existing conceptual models of FFWRS and to search for additional insightful perspectives. The initial research on FFWRS has been guided by a generic conceptual model of flood forecasting, flood warning dissemination and flood response (Figure 6.1). This process model is derived from existing research from a wide variety of sources with different disciplinary bases within the existing research literature which addresses hazard warnings (e.g. Williams 1964, McLuckie 1973, Foster 1980, Krzysztofowicz and Davis 1983, Smith and Handmer 1986, and Handmer and Penning-Rowsell 1990).

Within the initial process model the main components are forecasting, warning and response. Information flow is either intrinsic, that is, when it is part of the FFWRS and incorporating 'official' or authoritative warnings of floods; or extrinsic, involving 'unofficial' warnings used by flood plain users. These unofficial warnings are stimulated by perceived environmental hazard conditions and warning cues. There are also important feedback loops in the initial model.

An objective of the research is to subject the components of the process model (Figure 6.1) to closer scrutiny by the examination of existing empirical research results, and by comparison with practice as revealed through new empirical research. In this way the model may be expanded, and factors can be identified which are important to the effectiveness of FFWRS.

A complementary guiding conceptual perspective is Lazarus's (1966) stress model (Figure 6.2). In this model stress is a function of the challenge or demand of the event (i.e. the flood) and the

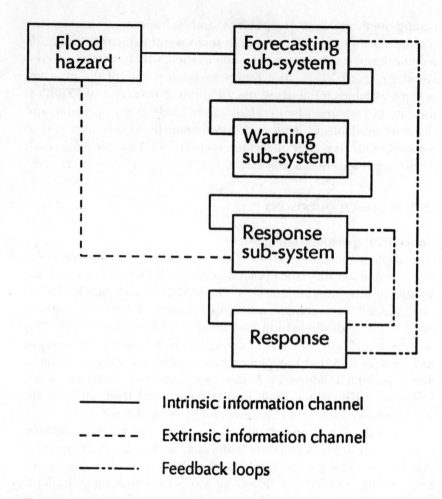

Intrinsic information channel

Extrinsic information channel

Feedback loops

Figure 6.1: Initial general conceptual model of FFWRS.

resources available to meet the challenge (Green 1991). In this simple but useful conceptualisation the challenge is determined by the flood characteristics (rate of rise, flood depth, velocity of flood water, flood duration, etc.) and for every possible challenge there are one or more appropriate adaptations (e.g. prevent water from entering property, raise property contents and evacuation). To be effective, each adaptation has certain requirements (warning lead time, prior information, etc.). Thus FFWRS need to be matched to both flood characteristics and adaptive response requirements. An objective of

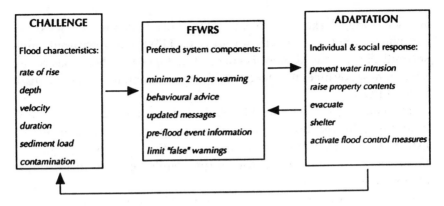

Figure 6.2: The Lazarus (1966) stress model.

the research is to identify these requirements so that FFWRS may be better matched to circumstances.

The objectives and benefits of FFWRS

The objectives of FFWRS also express the potential benefits of such systems. Flood forecasting, warning and response systems have been developed in different socio-cultural, economic and political settings, which provide the context in which the objectives and the benefits of FFWRS are expressed. Our research therefore focuses upon identifying the range of these objectives and benefits, and the different interests to which the benefits accrue. Flood forecasting, warning and response systems have the potential for delivering important benefits to communities. In some locations flood zone users expect to be warned of flooding by an authoritative, official source; in other locations such an expectation may not be present. Overall, the potential benefits of effective flood forecasts and warnings are reduced vulnerability to floods (Figure 3.1).

The measurement of FFWRS effectiveness

An important research question concerns the concept of effectiveness in the context of FFWRS – or how the effectiveness of a FFWRS might be measured.

There is a wide variety of possibilities here, ranging from technical measures such as actual flood levels compared with those forecasted, to economic measures such as the flood losses avoided, and measures of consumer satisfaction as expressed by flood zone users (Penning-

Rowsell 1986, Parker and Neal 1990). This research first seeks to determine whether the effectiveness of FFWRS is measured and, secondly, how measurement is currently achieved. It then goes on to suggest how advances in effectiveness measurement might be pursued in the future.

The central problem with FFWRS is that the benefits are not automatically delivered once a flood forecasting system has been established. There are a number of reasons for this. Considerable investment may go into flood forecasting whilst comparatively little attention or investment goes into warning dissemination and response. The process of flood forecasting may be prone to error and uncertainty. The formulation of flood warning messages is not straightforward, and raises a series of problems which are central to risk communication (Handmer and Penning-Rowsell 1990). The dissemination of flood warnings to those who need them is often a complex process involving many communication links and several different agencies (Penning-Rowsell *et al.* 1983).

Furthermore, physical flood-producing factors may combine to produce rapid responses of flooding to rainfall, making warning dissemination problematic. Response to flood warnings is a behavioural process in which a series of variables interacting with each other determine the adequacy of response. In practice, making FFWRS work effectively can prove to be a complicated process involving regular feedback and concerted interagency cooperation and learning over time.

The comparison of FFWRS practices between countries
A hypothesis underlying our research is that the performance of established and implemented FFWRS will vary according to a number of physical, cultural and organisational factors which collectively determine FFWRS effectiveness. The performance of FFWRS is expected to vary from total failure to near perfection. Given sufficient research, it should therefore be possible to isolate the conditions which on the one hand will lead to under-performance – and even to failure – and on the other hand to satisfactory performance.

A central expectation within our research on FFWRS is that, because of different physical, cultural, economic and institutional circumstances and experiences, countries in the European Union will have developed FFWRS to different levels – including different levels of effectiveness. When different circumstances are taken into account, comparison of the different experiences of countries provides important opportunities for improving practice and policies. This may be achieved by highlighting common problems, pooling knowledge and – with appropriate caution – identifying the most effective systems and best practices which might be transposed fruitfully from one country to another.

RESEARCH METHODS

Expanding the conceptual base

The conceptual research undertaken comprised several inter-related approaches, all underpinned by the reanalysis of existing empirical data and theoretical models and by the collection of new material. In the following discussion our first and third research components (the development of a generic model and reanalysis of existing data) will be discussed together, since they are closely interlinked.

One approach involves further testing and expanding the initial generic conceptual model (Figure 6.1), based upon further examination of the literature and research data available at a preliminary stage. First, FFWRS are conceptualised as a response to climate change and it is useful to identify the principal functions of FFWRS in this context. Secondly, it is useful to develop a single conceptual framework for the process associated with FFWRS which is generally applicable to the range of countries being studied. Thirdly, the main components of the conceptual model are expanded and the activities associated with each component and the principal agencies and stakeholders involved at various stages are identified in greater depth. Lastly, it is necessary to begin to identify the factors which existing empirical research reveals are important to the effectiveness of FFWRS.

A second approach involves conceptualising the development of FFWRS as a staged process. This is a pre-requisite for the cross-country comparisons of FFWRS. Such a staged development model of FFWRS (Table 6.1) usefully complements the process model. There appears to be a measure of consistency in how FFWRS are developed. This idea has been explored in order to identify the likely path of development of FFWRS from 'rudimentary' to 'advanced'. This developmental model provides the basis for a normative approach to FFWRS

Table 6.1: A staged development model of FFWRS.

Development stage	Characteristics of FFWRS in a country
1 Rudimentary	FFWRS are largely unused, but unofficial flood warning and response occurs. Less than 10% of geographical area served by FFWRS. FFWRS are almost entirely forecast-dominated but forecasting methods are rudimentary. The legal underpinning of FFWRS is weak, powers are mainly permissive and there is no liability for error. Where FFWRS exist warnings are untargeted, general ones either generally broadcast or communicated using primitive means. There is a closed approach towards making flood risk information available and no attempt to educate the public about flood hazards. FFWRS are assumed to be effective; there is no performance measurement, and no question of identifying standards. FFWRS agencies act independently; rivalry exists rather than effective cooperation.
2 Beginnings of FFWRS development	FFWRS are largely unused, but efforts to increase use of FFWRS identifiable. Unofficial flood warnings and response in use. Less than 25% of geographical area served by FFWRS. FFWRS remain forecast-dominated but some recognition of need to improve warning dissemination and/or response. Forecasting methods starting to be improved beyond rudimentary; maybe weather radar being installed in pilot locations. Some legal basis to FFWRS. Warnings remain largely untargeted and communicated by primitive means. Closed approach public flood risk information, no or little attempt to educate the public about flood hazards. Possibly some recognition of the ineffectiveness of FFWRS, but no formal means of feeding back lessons of failures. No performance targets or standards identifiable. FFWRS agencies act independently; rivalry rather than cooperation rules.
3 Intermediate	A FFWRS philosophy or approach is clearly identifiable, as are efforts to enhance FFWRS. Unofficial flood warnings and response in use. More than 25% but less than 50% of geographical area served by FFWRS. FFWRS are no longer forecast-dominated; attention is focused upon the warning dissemination problem and improving public response. A mixture of forecasting methods is used ranging from rudimentary to relatively sophisticated; weather radar has spread. Laws defining responsibilities of some agencies may exist, but probably focus upon forecasting and less clear on warning dissemination and response. Warning officials fear legal liability for error. Some targeting of warnings with some messages carrying information on more precise location and timing of flooding. Warning dissemination agencies and agents are identifiable. Information on the flood hazard is generally available, though not yet utilised effectively although there is some attempt to inform public about flood warning procedures. The limitations of FFWRS are now fairly widely recognised, and there is some effective learning through hindsight review. A number of forecast orientated performance indicators are in use; regional standards possibly with national standards, may have been identified. Agencies understand the need for close liaison but liaison shortcomings remain.

4 Approaching advanced	Positive strategies are being adopted to enhance FFWRS, and significant advances have been achieved. FFWRS are no longer forecast-dominated; considerable attention has been given to improving both warning dissemination and response. Geographical coverage by FFWRS is greater than 50%. FFWRS have been enhanced through application of more sophisticated forecasting and communication technologies: the latter may be under experimentation. Legal responsibilities for forecasting, warning dissemination and response are clearly defined and legal liability for error is also clearer with agencies either indemnified for mistakes or liabilities constrained. Warning messages contain full information on location, timing, anticipated flood depths etc. The warning dissemination process is well defined and rehearsed. Relaxed attitudes towards availability of flood risk information and strategies used to educate public of both the flood risk and warning and response procedures. Effectiveness of FFWRS now defined and research commissioned and/or completed on performance of FFWRS. Research and hindsight review findings being used to improve FFWRS. National standards in place; agency liaison problems being ironed out.
5 Advanced	Clearly identifiable FFWRS philosophy in place for some time; approach is marked by balance between investment in forecasting and in warning and advanced response. Advanced technologies have been applied to FFWRS in the forecasting, warning and response phases. Geographical coverage of FFWRS is greater than 50%. Legal responsibilities for all phases of FFWRS are defined; legal liabilities are defined but limited through indemnity or other constraint. Warning messages are well targeted using reliable and detailed data-base; information in messages is full and includes behavioural advice. Warning dissemination methods include use of modern technologies such as automatic telephone systems and pagers. Property owners may obtain full information on their risk of flooding and this information is publicly accessible. Flood plain users are regularly and fully informed of flood warning and response procedures and can obtain personal advice. A national strategy for measuring FFWRS effectiveness is in place, with performance targets set for future improvements. Performance indicators extend to warning dissemination and to response. There is close liaison and regular rehearsal between FFWRS agencies.

practice and policy development in the European Union.

The reanalysis of existing data sets on FFWRS is based upon the UK data sets held by Middlesex University Flood Hazard Research Centre. These data sets are available by virtue of approximately ten years of research in over ten locations in England and Wales. The original research focused either on flood damages or upon flood warnings, but in all cases broadly comparable data were obtained upon flood warnings and response. The cases reanalysed included those where there was a total failure of FFWRS and where FFWRS operated with different degrees of success. The objective of the reanalysis is to provide insight into the matching of FFWRS to both flood characteristics and adaptive response requirements.

An additional data set from France (Torterotot *et al.* 1992, Torterotot 1993), principally on the determinants of flood damage, also provides information on flood characteristics, warnings and response. This data set is used in this research to gain a degree of comparability and additional insight into the range of response behaviours following floods of different types, such as slow and rapid onset floods, and into the effects of behaviour and flood conditions on damage. The data are from eight riverine locations in France where the floods of the 1980s were investigated.

Methods for cross-country comparison

A number of methods were combined to gather data to enable comparisons of alternative FFWRS policy and practice across the European Union. The first stage comprised the construction of pre-liminary information profiles containing basic standardised information for each of the five countries: France, Germany, Portugal, the Netherlands and the United Kingdom. Data availability varied greatly between countries. However, the preliminary information profiles identified the following for each country:

- a national typology of floods;
- flood management institutions including laws and organisational responsibilities for FFWRS, and FFWRS components;
- perceived FFWRS performance indicators;
- the position of FFWRS within overall flood hazard management systems;
- lists of names and addresses and other contact details of proposed key informants;
- details of relevant legislation; and
- key literature.

The second stage involves using the staged development model of FFWRS constructed in the conceptual phase (Table 6.1). From the model a criteria-development matrix (CDM) was developed (Table 6.2). An interview and data collection checklist was constructed for a more penetrating analysis of FFWRS in each country through in-depth interviews with key informants (Chatterton 1994, Handmer

Table 6.2: Criteria-development matrix.

Characteristics or criteria	Development stages				
	1	2	3	4	5
1. Flood warning philosophy	Rudimentary		Inter-mediate		Advanced
2. Dominance of forecasting vs warning	Forecast dominant		Equal		Equal & improved accuracy
3. Application of technology to FFWRS	Model with manual extrapolation		Mixture		Fully automated
4. Geographical coverage	<10%		<50%		>50%
5. Laws relating to FFWRS	No laws/ permissive		Laws		Laws with liability
6. Content of warning messages to public	'Blanket': general location		Mixed: location/ timing		'Target': severity/ location & timing
7. Methods of disseminating flood warning	General broadcast		Wardens/ agencies/ police		Personal phone/fax/ pager
8. Attitudes to freedom of risk/hazard information	Little request only		Restricted to general flood plain		Open specific property
9. Public education about warnings	Minimum		Some, e.g. colour codes		Fully informed
10. Knowledge of FFWRS effectiveness	Denial of failure		Recognise limitations		Research tested
11. Dissemination of lessons learned	Little		Partial		Full
12. Performance targets and monitoring	None		Key indicators only		Accuracy/ timely/ reliable
13. National standards	Parochial		National/ regional variations		National/ international
14. Organisational culture	Independent		Agency liaison		Service level agreement with agencies

1: Basic-little development
3: Improved performance but some failures apparent
5: More advanced performance; failures reduced

1994). The design of this checklist was based principally upon the UK research experience of the Middlesex University Flood Hazard Research Centre. In the United Kingdom itself, our research with key informants focused principally upon Scotland and Northern Ireland – where there are information gaps – rather than upon England and Wales.

The data collection checklist comprised the following principal items:

- further identification of the characteristics of flood hazard problems;
- more detailed specification of the institutional context, including cultural factors which shape the approach to FFWRS;
- the objectives of flood hazard management;
- the 'political economy' of the country, with special reference to the way in which FFWRS are situated within the country's specific policy framework and how the development of FFWRS relates to important current policy debates, shifts and developments;
- the way in which sustainability issues and climate change are being incorporated into flood hazard management;
- the way in which the European Union has influenced policy developments relating to FFWRS;
- national and regional policy statements on FFWRS;
- any identification of the principal 'actors' or 'stakeholders' and their roles;
- the design of flood warning systems, and the major design issues;
- how FFWRS are designed, what constitutes 'good' performance and effectiveness, and what are considered as 'best practices';
- the strengths and weaknesses of FFWRS including a preliminary qualitative assessment of the level of development of FFWRS within each country according to fourteen criteria set out in matrix form;
- the identification of key literature and documents;
- a summary of the methodology, including the assessment matrix and reconceptualisation of FFWRS; and
- an identification of further research needs.

A crucial part of the approach is the selection of key informants. Key informants are defined as experienced individuals – usually officials but including researchers – who through their status, position of responsibility and/or knowledge, have both a strong insight into and overview of the operation and effectiveness of FFWRS in their country. In selecting key informants care was taken to include individuals from the principal agencies and stakeholders involved in FFWRS, where possible including informants at different organisational levels. With the help of our EUROflood collaborators and others, considerable effort was made to identify and interview these individuals. The following numbers of key informants were interviewed in each country: France 20, Germany 10, Portugal 15, the Netherlands 9, and the United Kingdom 11.

The criteria-development matrix (CDM)

The CDM (Table 6.2) is used to assess qualitatively the current state of development of FFWRS in each of the five countries. In the case of Germany, the Netherlands and the United Kingdom, within-country comparisons were also made. On the basis of previous research, fourteen criteria were identified by which the level of development of FFWRS may be gauged. The level of development (LoD) is gauged on a six-point categorical scale from 0 (rudimentary) through to 5 (advanced).

The criteria and the LoD scores reflect a normative perspective and it is important to explain this perspective. It is not the only one which may be formed, and the results strongly reflect this perspective. An important baseline for the analysis is that all five countries investigated are using FFWRS and are seeking to improve them.

We believe, within our perspective, that countries should have developed an explicit and coherent approach or philosophy towards FFWRS. This should either be reflected in official policy statements or articulated by key informants. Those countries in which such a philosophy is absent receive an LoD score of 0 or 1 on Criterion 1, whereas those which have explicitly focused upon flood warnings and have developed strong, explicit and coherent policies will receive scores of 4 or 5. Intermediate scores of 2 and 3 allow positions to be identified between these extremes.

Previous research reveals that a common reason for the underperformance of FFWRS is their domination by investment in forecasting technologies and the comparative neglect of warning dissemination and response. But improved performance comes with investment in forecasting *and* warning dissemination *and* response support systems. The LoD of a country is therefore gauged on Criterion

2 according to the degree to which FFWRS are 'forecast-dominated' (e.g. LoD 1 or 2) or otherwise.

Criterion 3 allows the application of technology to FFWRS to be scored focusing upon flood forecasting and warning dissemination. Where forecasting and warning methods remain rudimentary a score of 1 or 2 is given, depending on whether or not progress is being made. Where more advanced flood forecasting and communication methods are employed, a higher score is given depending upon the LoD achieved.

Criterion 4 allows the extent of geographical coverage of a country by FFWRS to be gauged, based upon the perspective that a score of 5 reflects greater than 50 per cent coverage. A score of 1 is given for less than 10 per cent geographical coverage and so on. The extent to which FFWRS are legally underpinned is the subject of Criterion 5. The presence of statutes identifying duties and liabilities for FFWRS (in the areas of forecasting, warning and response) is viewed as a characteristic of an advanced LoD. The absence of legal liability or the absence of laws specifying duties, or treating responsibilities as permissive powers, leads to categorisation as less advanced.

Criterion 6 concerns the content of public flood warning messages, with targeted warnings being more advanced than 'blanket' warnings, and with the degree of advancement being dependent upon the extent of information contained in warnings on flood severity, location and timing. Similarly, with Criterion 7 – methods of disseminating flood warnings – conditions may vary from generally broadcasted warnings to personally targeted ones using modern personalised communication technologies.

Criteria 8 and 9 are about the availability of public information on the flood hazard and FFWRS. A well-informed public is one which is likely to respond more effectively than an ill-informed one. Therefore positive attitudes towards making flood risk information available and efforts to inform the public are interpreted as important characteristics of an advanced LoD (e.g. 4 or 5). Agencies which have a high degree of knowledge of the performance and limitations of FFWRS based upon research are viewed as more advanced than those without.

This is gauged by Criterion 10; a characteristic of FFWRS at an early stage of development is likely to be agency ignorance of FFWRS effectiveness and the denial of FFWRS failures (e.g. LoD 1 or 2). More advanced arrangements for FFWRS will be grounded in systems in which the lessons of failures and under-performance are disseminated and used to improve future performance (e.g. LoD 4 or 5): this is Criterion 11. An attribute of a more advanced approach to FFWRS will be the specification of performance targets, usually incorporating accuracy, timeliness and reliability measures targets, with regular monitoring of performance: Criterion 12. Flood forecasting, warning and response systems in their early stages of development are not usually characterised by a performance measurement approach. An advanced strategy for FFWRS is likely to be characterised by a high degree of management in which there is some degree of national or international consistency of FFWRS standards (e.g. LoD 4 or 5), whilst allowing appropriately for local conditions and variations to suit them. On the other hand, standards are likely to be variable and inconsistent when FFWRS are at an early stage of development (e.g. LoD 1 or 2).

Finally, previous research suggests that the characteristics of the organisational culture amongst those agencies engaged in FFWRS which must cooperate and work together is a factor in the overall success of FFWRS. Cultures in which agencies are fiercely independent, and in which there is intense interagency rivalry, are unlikely to be effective. On Criterion 14 such cultures receive a score of 1 or 2 depending upon circumstances. In contrast cultures which are characterised by a high degree of cooperation, interagency agreements and frequent joint rehearsals are likely to be more effective, and are scored 4 or 5.

Case studies and limitations

Limited additional small-scale case studies of flood warnings and response were undertaken to provide more detail and to ensure that the higher level, more generalised research findings are reliable and reflect reality and practice. These case studies are valuable because they provide an opportunity to confirm or otherwise adjust the generalised research findings.

However, we must recognise that our research methodologies suffer from limitations. The staged development model of FFWRS (Table 6.1) is based upon a normative perspective and is experimental. Hindsight reveals a number of shortcomings. The model may not include all of the important aspects of FFWRS or all criteria for assessing FFWRS.

For example, the completed research reveals two different methods of disseminating information, including warnings, about floods. 'Cascade' dissemination systems appear to be cumbersome (the Hamburg experience). The Dutch prefer 'circuit' warning systems instead, because they believe that they are more effective and have useful built-in redundancy. The CDM (Table 6.2) does not currently allow the penetration of this kind of issue, which appears crucial to effectiveness. Similarly, a principal problem in the Netherlands, which now impacts upon effectiveness, is public complacency about floods and a widespread belief in the infallibility of the coastal defences. Again this kind of issue is currently difficult to take into account in the CDM but could undermine FFWRS effectiveness.

Furthermore, the relationship between the staged development model and effectiveness is not simple. The model suggests that a country will have more effective FFWRS performance the higher it is scored within the CDM. Whilst this may be generally true, there is no guarantee that it will be so. Advanced predictive and communication technologies offer the potential for effective FFWRS, but some simple and direct FFWRS might on occasions perform more effectively. The German experience with hardware and communication failures in 1986 is evidence of this possibility.

The assessment of the LoD of FFWRS in each country using the CDM is generalised, and obscures within-country variations. In order to gain an insight into these within-country variations, for both Germany and the Netherlands the CDM was completed for a number of regions (three in Germany and four in the Netherlands).

The CDM assessment is based upon the information gained from the selected key informants and is dependent upon their responses. Other key informants may have different perspectives. However, it is believed that the key informant selection process used should provide a reliable picture. Some problems were encountered in applying the criteria and LoDs to each country with consistency, and although each criterion and LoD is defined, refinements are required.

The research is based upon existing empirical evidence and country overviews, with limited case study support. Important gaps exist in the existing empirical evidence. Most of the detailed survey data on FFWRS are available from England and Wales and from France. Whilst data sets contained data from surveys which are broadly comparable, differences in survey instruments and circumstances

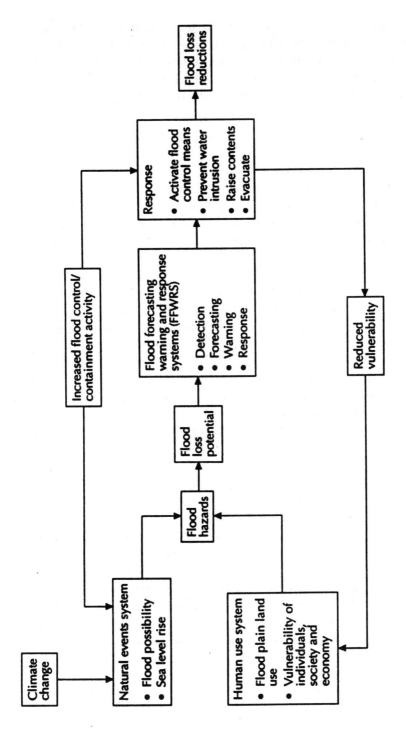

Figure 6.3: The potential role of FFWRS in responding to climate change through reducing vulnerability and enabling increased flood control/ containment activity.

make comparability a problem. Similar survey data are not yet available from Germany, the Netherlands and Portugal. In spite of the completion of several insightful case studies, the country overviews need complementing with further in-depth case studies which can penetrate further than is possible with the methodologies so far used.

RESEARCH RESULTS

The revised conceptual base

Flood forecasting, warning and response systems have an important role in responding to climate change, and this role is modelled in Figure 6.3. Such systems provide one response mechanism 'package' which can contribute to reducing potential flood losses in two principal ways.

As long as they operate effectively, FFWRS can substantially reduce the vulnerability of flood zones and their users to floods contributed to by sea-level rise. They may achieve this by enabling a series of vulnerability-reducing actions prior to flooding. The main response categories are: prevention of flood water intrusion, the lifting or raising of property contents, and the evacuation of both property contents and occupants to safe territory. Secondly, effective FFWRS are often also necessary to enable structural flood control measures to be operated. Flood control systems often include flood barriers and gates – an important form of flood protection in the European Union – which must be operated and closed prior to flooding. Even where there are fixed flood barriers (e.g. embankments or dikes) these will need constant monitoring, and maybe repair, for them to be effective. FFWRS are thus important to timely monitoring and repair and to the containment of floods.

On the basis of our research the initial generic process model of FFWRS has been expanded (Figure 6.4). A detection sub-system component has been added since this is regarded as a vital part of FFWRS, and the principal feedback loops have been modified in the light of further research evidence. The model has been expanded to include the principal activities involved in each component of the process, the principal agencies and stakeholders, and the factors which are considered important to inducing effectiveness. The staged development model of FFWRS marks a further conceptual advance.

The application of the Lazarus model serves to emphasise the complex reality of a flood event. Reanalysis of the available data sets (see also Chapter 3) has confirmed the damage-reducing potential of flood warnings but has also highlighted the widespread use of 'extrinsic' information channels and thus response in the absence of 'official' warnings. In order for FFWRS to increase efficiency in this respect there is a need for concerted public information and education programmes before flood events. This will enable flood victims to assess more adequately environmental cues prior to the receipt of warnings and to respond more effectively on receipt of warnings. Figure 6.2 indicates the minimum preferred criteria for an FFWRS.

The objectives and benefits of FFWRS

The objectives and benefits of FFWRS in the five European Union countries include national and regional security, general public security and safety, significantly reduced property damage, reduced stress and anxiety amongst flood zone users, the protection of industry dependent upon water levels, efficient waterway navigation, and reduced political risk.

To take the last of these, a benefit which may sometimes be perceived by flood plain managers or political decision makers is the avoidance or reduction of politically damaging disquiet and inquiry following a severe flood. FFWRS may sometimes be adopted by decision makers as a reactive, defensive political strategy.

There are important differences in the way in which FFWRS are 'embedded' within the culture and life of the five countries researched. Much is explained by historical experience of disasters in general and flood disasters in particular. The regional variation in this embedding is particularly acute in Scotland, for example. These differences strongly influence perceptions of the objectives and benefits of FFWRS.

There are three principal cases. With 60 per cent of the Netherlands below mean sea level, and a history of severe flood disasters (e.g. the 1953 disaster), flood protection and FFWRS are viewed as nationally and strategically important. Such systems are strongly linked to disaster planning and the mustering of dike armies is an important and emphasised response phase. On the coast the objective of FFWRS is to keep the country free from flooding.

Thus the principal function of FFWRS is resource mobilisation to prevent flooding. General public warnings in coastal areas of the

PRINCIPAL FFWRS COMPONENTS AND INFORMATION AND FEEDBACK SYSTEMS

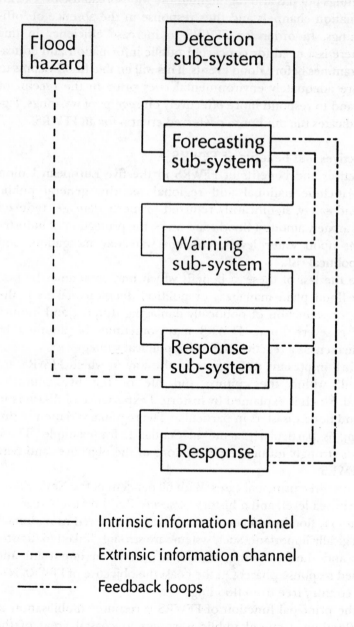

——————— Intrinsic information channel

- - - - - Extrinsic information channel

—·—·—· Feedback loops

Figure 6.4: Revised conceptual model of the FFWRS process and components.

PRINCIPAL ACTIVITIES	PRINCIPAL AGENCIES AND STAKEHOLDERS (GENERALISED)	KEY FACTORS INDUCING EFFECTIVENESS	
● Collection of meteorological data ● Weather forecasts ● Collection of hydrometric and hydrographic data ● Data collection	● Meteorological agency ● Central or state water/coastal management agency with regional/local units	● Telemetric data collection ● Dense networks of data collection stations ● Weather radar coverage to enhance rainfall/flood warning lead times	DETECTION SUB-SYSTEM
● Receiving and interpreting data ● Modelling of floods ● Flood forecasting, including updates ● Decision to issue warnings ● Issuing flood warnings, updates ● Liaison with other agencies	● Flood forecasting agency ● Central or state water/coastal management agency with regional/local units	● Computer coded rainfall/run-off and flood routeing modelling ● Real-time modelling ● Experienced flood forecasters ● Efficient inter-agency communication systems ● Limited or indemnified legal liability for error	FORECASTING SUB-SYSTEM
● Receiving flood forecasts and warnings ● Interpreting warnings, decision to warn down-line ● Dissemination of warnings ● Provide source of information ● Liaison with other agencies including media	● Regional/local government units ● Media ● Civil protection/civil defence agencies (e.g. fire, police)	● Unambiguous legal responsibilities for all FFWRS phases ● 24-hour staffed offices ● Minimal delays in passing information ● Efficient routeing of communications with in-built redundancy ● Long flood warning lead times ● Few "false warnings" ● Well-targeted warnings ● Forecasted flood levels, accurate timing information ● Efficient reports of flood plains/properties to be warned ● High level of interagency cooperation	WARNING SUB-SYSTEM
● Disseminate warnings and trigger responses within agencies (e.g. to monitor defences, close barriers, pump water, repair defences). ● Coordinate emergency response and activate emergency services ● Respond to public ● Provide information - liaise	● Regional water/coastal management or flood control agencies ● Local government units ● Civil protection/civil defence agencies (e.g. fire, police, ambulance) ● Local flood wardens	● Information confirmation service for the public ● Rehearsed response with learning feedback	RESPONSE SUB-SYSTEM
● Reduce vulnerability to damage and reduce damage through prevention of water intrusion, raising contents of properties, and evacuation	● River users ● Flood plain/flood zone users	● Availability of assistance ● Pre-flood warning awareness and understanding ● Prior flood experience ● Response information and rehearsals	RESPONSE

Netherlands mean that FFWRS have already failed. In Dutch river valleys the objective of FFWRS is different. It is to enable loss of life and property to be minimised. The Dutch flood prevention emphasis is also found to a lesser extent on the low-lying east coast of England, which also suffered severely in 1953. In the United Kingdom FFWRS are a vital component of tidal flooding exclusion using flood barriers (such as the Thames barrier which protects London) and the main objective is to prevent loss of life from sea flooding.

Objectives and perceived benefits of FFWRS are rather different in Germany. Here a key objective of FFWRS is to aid commercial waterway navigation (an important secondary but locally important objective in France and the United Kingdom). In Germany flood warnings to the general public are apparently currently considered as a secondary benefit, but they remain important for flood-prone communities.

In both the United Kingdom and France the principal objective of FFWRS in riverine locations is public safety and property damage reduction, and the alleviation of public anxiety and stress. To a lesser extent the same is true of Portugal, although currently FFWRS are less extensively developed there. Such systems are now closely linked to natural disaster planning in France, but in the United Kingdom the links with civil emergency planning are under-developed.

The measurement of FFWRS effectiveness
The measurement of the effectiveness of FFWRS is currently under-developed in the countries researched. Post-event audits are relatively uncommon. This is especially the case with the warning dissemination and response components of FFWRS. Performance targets are rarely set in terms of the requirements of those at risk. Benefit-cost or cost-effectiveness analyses of FFWRS are rare although such an analysis is to be commissioned in Scotland. Improvements to FFWRS are usually based on political judgements, often without an assessment of the accuracy or reliability of FFWRS.

In France flood forecasting agencies measure effectiveness principally in terms of the quantified tolerances of the predicted flood water depth and time. These types of performance indicators are also common elsewhere. There are currently several tests of effectiveness in the Netherlands, although audits are patchy. Here the prime test of effectiveness in coastal areas is the degree to which timely warnings can prevent breaching of the dike-rings. The aim is to achieve a 6-hour warning lead time for predicted levels for 70 per cent of the time.

In inland riverine zones in the Netherlands success is judged through communication with customers about predictive model improvements, but in Rotterdam there is no audit of the receipt of warning messages by flood plain users. In Portugal there is general acknowledgement of the limitations of the existing FFWRS. Here there is little evidence of effectiveness measurement, although the weather radar extension project has performance targets for prediction accuracy and timeliness. Apart from comparing predicted and actual flood levels, in Germany improvements to effectiveness are considered principally in terms of technological advances designed to increase warning lead times.

Germany, England and Wales are researching or using FFWRS performance targets relating to reliability, accuracy and timeliness. For example, Hamburg evaluates the success of flood warnings after each event using these indicators. In England and Wales a national research project has proposed normative targets for FFWRS based upon these indicators. In the Highland region of Scotland performance was measured in the past by the extent of catchment area estimated to require a flood warning against the area for which flood warnings were provided. More recently it has been taken as the number of flood warnings anticipated to be required in a given year against the number of flood warnings actually issued.

Comparisons of the level of development of FFWRS in five European Union countries

The CDM (Table 6.2) has been used to compare FFWRS policy and practice in each of the five countries. The results (Figures 6.5–6.9) should be interpreted cautiously and within the context of our clearly stated limitations of both the staged development model for FFWRS and the CDM methodology (see above).

The results indicate two broad categories of development amongst the five countries. In general terms France, Germany, the Netherlands and the United Kingdom appear to have reached the third or fourth stage of development upon many criteria, whilst Portugal appears to have reached a slightly lower level of development. However, in Portugal recognition of the limitations of FFWRS is relatively high

Development stages

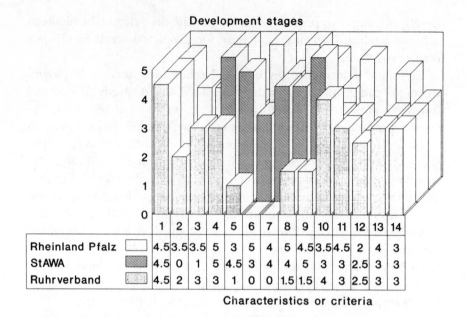

	1	2	3	4	5	6	7	8	9	10	11	12	13	14
Rheinland Pfalz	4.5	3.5	3.5	5	3	5	4	5	4.5	3.5	4.5	2	4	3
StAWA	4.5	0	1	5	4.5	3	4	4	5	3	3	2.5	3	3
Ruhrverband	4.5	2	3	3	1	0	0	1.5	1.5	4	3	2.5	3	3

Characteristics or criteria

Figure 6.5: Development stages of FFWRS – Germany.

and improvement initiatives are being pursued. There appears to be particularly wide variation in the extent to which FFWRS are legally underpinned (Criterion 5). Germany, France and the United Kingdom have FFWRS in which forecast-domination no longer occurs, whereas the Netherlands appears to have advanced furthest in this respect.

Small-scale case studies

Our series of small-scale case studies is complete and provides additional insight into the structure of FFWRS, experience including current difficulties and failures, responses which may become more dependent upon FFWRS, and new initiatives. The following are amongst those case studies we have completed, further details of which are in the technical annexes which accompany this volume.

1. The River Garonne (France) – short flood warning lead times. An example of the technologies required to forecast and respond to flash floods, the enhancements in progress, the warning dissemination chain and the difficulties experienced with using telephone answering machines.

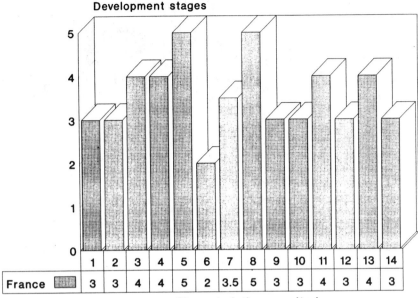

Figure 6.6: Development stages of FFWRS – France.

2. The River Seine (France) – long flood warning lead times. A contrasting case to the Garonne and one where navigation as well as flood damage reduction needs are considered to be important. Forecasting is manual and based on information from historic floods. The Seine is currently considered too complex for fully accurate mathematical modelling. Currently the automated hydrological data collection equipment has a relatively high failure rate. Communication links in data collection are duplicated to increase reliability. Problems existed with warning dissemination on some of the faster responding tributaries because of six-hour delays in satellite transmission and the lack of suitable radio frequencies in the Paris region. However, the use now of specialised telephone lines is believed to have addressed these problems.

3. Rotterdam (the Netherlands) – flood warning procedures. An example of a triumvirate management team approach to FFWRS in which flood warning information is passed back and forth in a circuit communication system. This communication is believed to avoid communication oversight or failure.

4. Maastricht (the Netherlands) – flood warning process. An

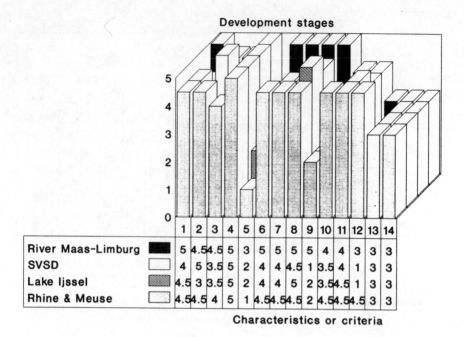

		1	2	3	4	5	6	7	8	9	10	11	12	13	14
River Maas-Limburg	■	5	4.5	4.5	5	3	5	5	5	5	4	4	3	3	3
SVSD	□	4	5	3.5	5	2	4	4	4.5	1	3.5	4	1	3	3
Lake Ijssel	▨	4.5	3	3.5	5	2	4	4	5	2	3.5	4.5	1	3	3
Rhine & Meuse	▤	4.5	4.5	4	5	1	4.5	4.5	5	2	4.5	4.5	4.5	3	3

Characteristics or criteria

Figure 6.7: Development stages of FFWRS – The Netherlands.

example of a flood forecasting, warning and response system which experiences difficulties because liaison over data for flood forecasting with a partner European Union country (Belgium) is inadequate. Cross-river cooperation is claimed to be poor and Flanders has a different flood hazard philosophy.

5. The Landerarbeitsgemeinschaft Wasser-LAWA (Germany) – comparative survey of the present state of flood warning services in Germany. A federal working group draft report which reveals some current confusion of interpretation in cross-boundary, cross-border situations between *Landes* over the various levels for flood warnings. Standardisation and consistency is recommended, and greater international cooperation is required. The research also provides an overview of variability in flood forecasting methods used on major rivers in Germany.

6. The High Water Warning Centre at Karlsruhe, Baden Wurttemberg (Germany) – example of state-of-the-art forecasting and warning dissemination service. An example of a system designed to optimise flood retention in reservoirs. Automatic alarms from fifty gauging stations automatically alarm the police and local

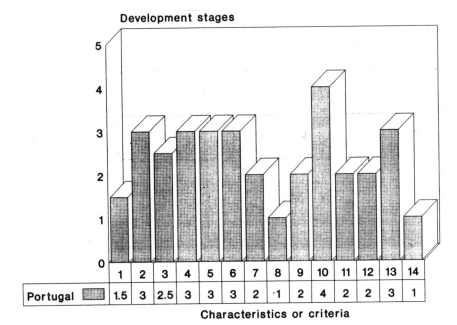

Development stages

Portugal	1	2	3	4	5	6	7	8	9	10	11	12	13	14
	1.5	3	2.5	3	3	3	2	·1	2	4	2	2	3	1

Characteristics or criteria

Figure 6.8: Development stages of FFWRS – Portugal.

officials if prescribed water levels are reached. Mayors may then activate local hazard plans. The forecasting centre gives information to the general public through BtX and teletext and so on, and has a high public relations profile. Flood warnings are targeted to groups of potential flood victims. The forecasting team comprises a hydrologist, an engineer and an information scientist.

7. The Towyn flood of February 1990 (United Kingdom: Wales) – sea flood in which FFWRS failures occurred. An example of shortcomings in the flood warning dissemination process owing to warning agency offices not being staffed on a 24-hour basis and various delays in passing on flood warnings.

8. Floodgate closures in seawall flood defences (United Kingdom: England) – dependence upon FFWRS. An example of the considerable number of flood gate systems in coastal defences around the United Kingdom. The coast of the county of Essex is believed to have about two hundred such gates, each of which needs to be closed to make flood defences secure. Responsibility for closing these gates is fragmented amongst a large number of individuals and organisations. A range of failure scenarios is

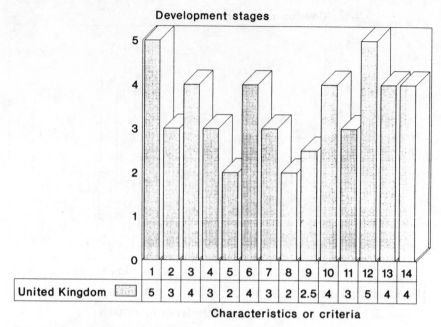

United Kingdom	1	2	3	4	5	6	7	8	9	10	11	12	13	14
	5	3	4	3	2	4	3	2	2.5	4	3	5	4	4

Characteristics or criteria

Figure 6.9: Development stages of FFWRS – United Kingdom.

possible. Sea-level rise could result in a requirement for increased frequency of closure.

9. The Perth, Scotland, floods of January 1993 (United Kingdom) – a study of dissemination and response in a recent flood event. This study focuses particularly on the actions of the emergency responders and on evacuation issues in the light of public misperceptions of the nature of the flood risk. Many reacted inappropriately because they based their response on a previous flood event where they personally did not get flooded.

10. The proposed radar-based flash flood forecasting system (Portugal) – example of new initiative. There are currently no warnings for flash floods affecting the Lisbon urban area. Precipitation measurement is the only way to provide flood warnings and a small research team is exploring the possibility of establishing a new radar system with appropriate precipitation and run-off forecasting models near Lisbon. This project is funded under EPOCH, in parallel with our own research.

CONCLUSIONS AND POLICY IMPLICATIONS

This chapter provides a relatively high level overview of FFWRS at the conceptual, practical and policy levels in five European Union countries. Overviews of this kind can make a significant contribution to the development of more effective FFWRS practices and policies in the European Union where collaborative approaches have so far been limited. This contribution may be developed through identifying and sharing common problems and solutions, and by identifying best practices and policies.

However, the overview approach contains risks associated with generalisation and obscuration of important details of problems, practices and policies. For this reason a series of case studies is incorporated to reveal important detail. They also allow generalisations to be checked, confirmed and adjusted. One problem is that policies agreed and established may not be effectively implemented. This is just one potential pitfall of the overview approach which needs supplementing by further carefully selected larger-scale in-depth case studies. Country overviews, and associated cross-country comparisons, may also obscure important within-country variations. These are revealed by our research on Germany, the Netherlands and the United Kingdom, and should be taken into account to qualify our generalisations.

Several conceptual frameworks are now available which are applicable to the European Union. These include a model of the role of FFWRS in relation to climate change and sea-level rise. A process model has been developed which now identifies the main components of FFWRS, supported by detailed country overview reports identifying, for example, the main agencies and stakeholders in each case. A staged development model provides a basis for normative policy suggestions and conclusions. The process and staged development models both now provide insight into the factors which are likely to induce FFWRS effectiveness.

Our conclusion from our research must be that the significance of historico-cultural settings to the positioning of FFWRS within a country's institutional and policy framework is emphasised by the country studies. These reveal both significantly different and similar objectives and expectations. This historico-cultural factor presents limits on the extent to which, and ways in which, FFWRS practices and policies may be transferred across the Union. Nevertheless, even when these important limits are recognised, there are many common FFWRS problems and characteristics.

In addition, we have found significant differences between formal ('intrinsic') and informal ('extrinsic') FFWRS systems, although the research focuses mainly upon 'intrinsic' FFWRS. Research data from the United Kingdom, France and elsewhere indicate that 'extrinsic' FFWRS are sometimes very important in reducing flood damage potential, especially for medium to slow rising floods and occasionally for flash floods. However, relatively few research data exist on 'extrinsic' systems in the Union. More data are required on the extent to which such systems can be relied upon, and in what circumstances. More consideration should be given to ways of supporting 'extrinsic' systems where they prove to be effective and to avoiding over-reliance upon 'intrinsic' systems where they might not be needed. Thus attention should be given to the line of reasoning which holds that 'official' development of FFWRS should not preclude effective self-help measures.

Another conclusion is that countries can learn from each other. The application of the staged development model and CDM suggests a comparatively large number of cross-country linkages may be made which could lead to transfer of practices and policies and the general raising of FFWRS standards and effectiveness in the Union. An obvious direction of linkage is between Portugal and the other four countries investigated. Some important linkages of this sort have already been established. The legal basis of FFWRS varies enormously across the Union; all countries face a common or similar public flood hazard and flood warning education problem; all countries face similar problems relating to performance measurement; most countries face problems in adequately targeting flood warnings; and so on.

There is also a wealth of experience with communication methods and technologies, and the problems and opportunities which they present. Further comparison of 'cascade' and 'circuit' communication systems is required. The need for rapid, simultaneous mass communication between warning agencies and the public is a common one and may well benefit from a common strategy. The use of automated flood warning systems, such as those operating in parts of Germany, needs to be investigated for possible application elsewhere in the Union. Above all, it takes considerable time to develop FFWRS, and progress is usually made by incremental steps. The pace of FFWRS development could be increased through cross-country collaboration.

Another conclusion is that, currently, there appears to be relatively little knowledge about the effectiveness of end-user response to flood warnings and the most appropriate response strategies for particular types of circumstances (both flooding conditions and social conditions). Here, the application of the Lazarus model can provide insight. Viewing the FFWRS as an intervening variable between challenge and adaptation creates the possibility of countering possibly inaccurate 'commonsense' assumptions and responses with appropriate and targeted behavioural advice. The research on flood gates demonstrates that there may be important organisational and institutional problems associated with response to secure sea defences in England. Here, comparison with the Netherlands may prove fruitful.

Our research results also suggest that a strategy is required in which the effectiveness and performance of each of the principal components of FFWRS is routinely measured. Existing performance baselines must be identified and performance targets set. Effectiveness indicators should reflect forecasting, warning dissemination and the response phases, and should include the requirements of flood plain users.

A significant additional problem area revealed by the research, and not currently dealt with adequately in the staged development model and CDM, is cross-border liaison and cooperation where rivers form the border between states or where rivers pass through one state after another. This problem arises in Germany, France, Belgium, the Netherlands and Portugal and further research is required to reveal its extent and to propose solution strategies.

REFERENCES

Chatterton, J.B. (1994) *EUROflood Country Reports for Germany and the Netherlands.* Internal report to Middlesex University Flood Hazard Research Centre

Foster, H.D. (1980) *Disaster Planning: the preservation of life and property.* Berlin, Germany: Springer Verlag

Green, C. (1991) Enabling Effective Hazard Management by the Public. In Parker, D. and Handmer, J. (eds) *Hazard Management and Emergency Planning:*

perspectives on Britain, 175–93. London, UK: James and James

Handmer, J.W. (1994) EUROflood Country Reports for France and Portugal. Internal report to Middlesex University Flood Hazard Research Centre

Handmer, J.W. and Penning-Rowsell, E.C. (eds) (1990) *Hazards and the Communication of Risk*. Aldershot, UK: Gower Technical Press

Krzysztofowicz, R. and Davis, R. (1983) A Methodology for Evaluation of Flood Forecast-response Systems. *Water Resources Research*, 19 (6) 1423–54

Lazarus, R.S. (1966) *Psychological Stress and the Coping Process*. New York, USA: McGraw-Hill

McLuckie, B.J. (1973) *The Warning System in Disaster Situations: a selective analysis*. Disaster Research Center Research Series, no. 9. Ohio, USA: Ohio State University

Parker, D.J. and Neal, J. (1990) Evaluating the Performance of Flood Warning Systems. In Handmer, J.W. and Penning-Rowsell, E.C. (eds) *Hazard and the Communication of Risk*, 137–56. Aldershot, UK: Gower Technical Press

Penning-Rowsell, E.C. (1986) The Development of Integrated Flood Warning Systems. In Smith, D.I. and Handmer, J.W. (eds) *Flood Warning in Australia*, 15–36. Canberra, Australia: Centre for Resource and Environmental Studies, Australian National University

Penning-Rowsell, E.C.; Parker, D.J.; Crease, D. and Mattison, C.R. (1983) *Flood Warning Dissemination: an evaluation of some current practices in the Severn-Trent Water Authority area*. Geography and Planning Papers, no. 7. London, UK: Middlesex University, Flood Hazard Research Centre

Saul, A.J. (1992) *Floods and Flood Management*. Dordrecht, Netherlands: Kluwer Academic Publishers

Smith, D.I. and Handmer, J.W. (eds) (1986) *Flood Warning in Australia*. Canberra, Australia: Centre for Resource and Environmental Studies, Australian National University

Torterotot, J.P. (1993) *Le cout des dommages dus aux inondations: estimation et analyse des incertitudes* (The cost of damage due to flooding: assessment and uncertainty analysis). Doctoral thesis. Paris, France: Ecole Nationale des Ponts et Chaussées

Torterotot, J.P.; Kauark-Leite, L.A. and Roche, P.A. (1992) Analysis of Individual Real-time Responses to Flooding and Influence on Damage to Households. In Saul, A.J. (ed.) *Floods and Flood Management*, 363–87. Dordrecht, Netherlands: Kluwer Academic Publishers

Williams, H.B. (1964) Human Factors in Warning-and-response Systems. In Grosser, G.; Wechsler, H. and Greenblatt, M. (eds) *The Threat of Impending Disaster: contributions to the psychology of stress*. Cambridge, Mass, USA: Massachusetts Institute of Technology (MIT) Press

CHAPTER 7

The Planning of Flood Alleviation Measures: Interface with the Public

Francisco Nunes Correia, Maria da Graça Saraiva, João Rocha, Maureen Fordham, Fátima Bernardo, Isabel Ramos, Zulmira Marques and Luís Soczka

INTRODUCTION

Context and aims

The social and psychological dimensions associated with floods are becoming increasingly recognised as important aspects of flood hazard management. The understanding of how people evaluate and respond to natural hazards such as floods is important for the adoption of adequate and viable counter-flood measures, both in structural and non-structural terms. Thus, the adoption of engineering approaches and solutions must be associated with and complemented by tools provided by the cognitive sciences, namely psychology and sociology.

The aim of this chapter is to elucidate our understanding of how people evaluate and respond to natural hazards such as floods, and how this knowledge can be integrated into the planning and management process. Such an approach demands a clear comprehension of the processes of the perception of risks, causal attributions and possible solutions to the hazard problem; and an understanding of patterns of behaviour and action adopted during hazard situations. Furthermore, it is necessary to examine the previous initiatives and the future willingness of the public to participate in planning flood control measures.

A case study is highlighted to address the range of factors concerned. First, the Livramento river catchment and the population of the Portuguese town of Setúbal living in this catchment were chosen to examine public perception of flood hazards in a southern European context. This case study focuses on issues of public involvement in the planning stages of flood alleviation measures and in particular it examines the use of geographic information systems (GIS) and other computer graphic devices as a tool for integrating flood and land use planning information and interacting with the public (Figure 7.1). Secondly, for comparative purposes we also look at complementary research from cases in the United Kingdom to indicate the different perceptions of rivers and flood management by professionals and the general public in a different cultural and climatic environment.

Public perception and participation: the need for understanding
Public participation is an important component at all stages of the implementation of water resource management projects. This is particularly apparent in the case of flood protection measures, which can be very controversial. The implementation of structural flood defence measures, in particular, can have considerable environmental and social impacts, and in the absence of an accurate public

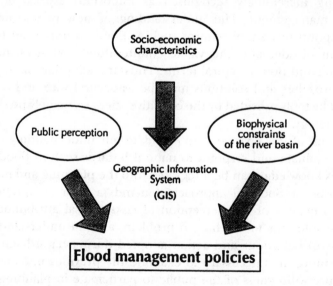

Figure 7.1: GIS as a tool for an integrated approach.

perception of flood risk there can be significant opposition to, and a lack of positive engagement with, any proposed measures.

Furthermore, non-structural measures, such as land use planning mechanisms or flood warning schemes, are becoming increasingly important elements of flood hazard policies (see Chapter 6) and, in order to operate effectively, these policy approaches demand even greater collaboration with the affected population and numerous interconnecting agencies than do traditional structural measures. Also, appropriate behaviour during the occurrence of flood events (as with other natural hazards) is an important element in the minimisation of losses; we need to understand this behaviour.

Additionally, we need to codify existing public knowledge and experience. Flood hazards are one of the natural hazards better understood by local – riverine – populations. The presence of the river can be a useful reminder of the dangerous situations that may occur; risk awareness is raised, appropriate coping behaviour is developed and willingness to participate in any process of public involvement in flood management is, in principle, more likely to occur. However, in the case of many southern European rivers, the ephemeral nature of watercourses may mean, for much of the year, that this trigger to risk perception is not explicit. Thus, within the countries of the European Union, the river and its associated flood plain may have a range of perceived functions and threats dependent upon a complex interaction of differing physical, socio-economic and cultural factors.

THE ENVIRONMENTAL AND DECISION-MAKING CONTEXT: INSIGHTS FROM THE UNITED KINGDOM AND ELSEWHERE

The provision of flood protection for people at risk from flooding would appear to be an uncontentious act. However, on examination, it can be seen to be a complex land use planning issue, involving many potentially conflicting interests. The imposition on local communities of environmental change arising from structural flood defences can provoke emotional responses, particularly from those not adequately included in the planning process (Fordham 1993).

Increasingly in recent years there have been examples of a more proactive approach towards environmentally sensitive river engineering (Gardiner 1988, 1991) and also towards river rehabilitation and

restoration (ECON 1993, Saraiva *et al.* 1992). This approach emphasises the management of rivers and flood plains without destroying
their ecological, aesthetic and cultural qualities. Furthermore, these
new initiatives also emphasise the importance of including public
consultation and participation in the planning process.

Throughout Europe (as elsewhere) there has been an increase in
the growth of interest groups and community activism, particularly
related to issues of environmental concern. Recent studies in the
United Kingdom have shown that the ecological, amenity and cultural
value of the river environment is such that many flood plain
occupants would rather live with the flood risk than accept structural
flood defences which they perceive will have major deleterious
impacts on their local environment (Fordham 1992, Tapsell *et al.*
1991, Tunstall and Fordham 1990). In these studies the river is
perceived to be a positive environmental asset and people are in
effect willing to suffer more flooding in the higher environmental
quality areas; thus the risk-environment trade-off takes the form of
a reduction in the percentage of respondents who are willing to
live with the different floods as one moves away from the river
(Figure 7.2).

In Portugal, in contrast, there appears to be less awareness of the
potential for enhanced environments associated with river corridors,
and less of a culture of public participation in land use planning.
The expressions of environmental concern have yet to reach
similarly widespread levels of action and organisation to those in the
United Kingdom. However, it can be expected that this situation is
not static.

The environment does make a difference. In the Portuguese study
of Setúbal discussed in more detail below, the concrete-lined river
represents an environmental nuisance for a major part of the year.
When there is a low flow or no flow at all, sewage contamination
becomes obvious and the dumping of rubbish makes the river an eye-
sore. For the local riverine population there is the additional problem
of flooding during times of heavy rainfall. Thus sensitive river
management is not seen as a priority and culverting and flood plain
development can appear a better option (there are degraded river
environments in the United Kingdom where similarly radical management options would also be welcomed).

Attitudes do change, however, even if slowly. In the 1980s and 1990s

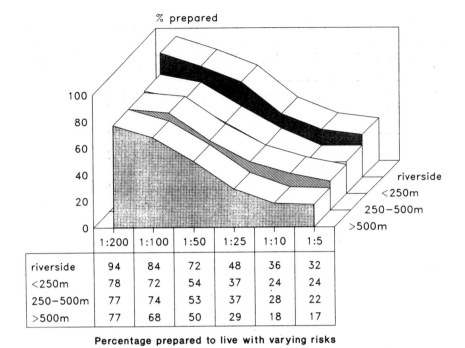

% prepared	1:200	1:100	1:50	1:25	1:10	1:5
riverside	94	84	72	48	36	32
<250m	78	72	54	37	24	24
250–500m	77	74	53	37	28	22
>500m	77	68	50	29	18	17

Percentage prepared to live with varying risks

Figure 7.2: Preparedness to live with varying flood risks by distance from the river (1989).

river engineering has become more sensitive to landscape values and ecological interest (Gardiner 1991, 1988) and the perceived options for managing the river in partnership with nature have increased. Indeed, many river engineers regard themselves as 'environmentalists', although in this context the term encompasses dimensions of control and utility that can conflict with the concerns of some flood plain residents for whom aesthetic, cultural and even bio-ethical issues are paramount (Fordham 1992). Attitudes also differ between professionals and the public. Thus there is a considerable literature examining and highlighting the differences in perception and attitude between professionals of various kinds and the public (White 1966a, 1966b, Craik 1970, Sewell 1971, 1974, Sewell and Little 1973, Cotgrove 1982, Fordham 1992, 1993). Of particular relevance here is the tendency among professionals to prioritise technical elements over more subjective elements in decision making; they have a preference for retaining control over option generation and public information dissemination, and a resistance to institutional change.

Therefore, while there may have been improvements in environmental engineering technology, in general there has been less progress in methods of public consultation and environmental mediation. Whilst public consultation is now an accepted element in much flood defence scheme promotion, the timing of such consultation generally remains fixed at a relatively late stage when many decisions have already been taken. In contrast, research in the United Kingdom has found that the public generally prefers to be consulted at an early stage about such proposals (Figure 7.3).

Many professionals regard themselves as having the necessary skills and training to 'solve the problem' and prefer to enter the public decision-making arena with well-formed plans which they present to the general public for confirmation but not for debate. Such proposed solutions, imposed from outside, may not be publicly acceptable and may not function adequately if they also rely on a behavioural response from a public that has not been involved with their development.

The initiation of alternative programmes of public participation could entail fundamental changes in existing institutional and professional cultures to create more devolved power structures. Indeed, it is questionable whether existing models of the control of nature are environmentally, socially or economically sustainable without a radical re-examination of methods of public accountability and participation in decision making. In the light of the uncertain risks presented by global climate change, the need to address these issues becomes crucial if the environmental damage caused by previous generations of decision makers is to be avoided.

METHODS AND APPROACH: THE SETÚBAL EXAMPLE

The following sections present a brief methodological overview of the main research study components, including a description of the main Portuguese study site, the public perception studies of flood risks and solutions, the use of GIS as a tool to simulate and compare scenarios and for interfacing with the public, and the modelling of the physical system – including the hydrological and hydraulic aspects (Correia *et al.* 1992).

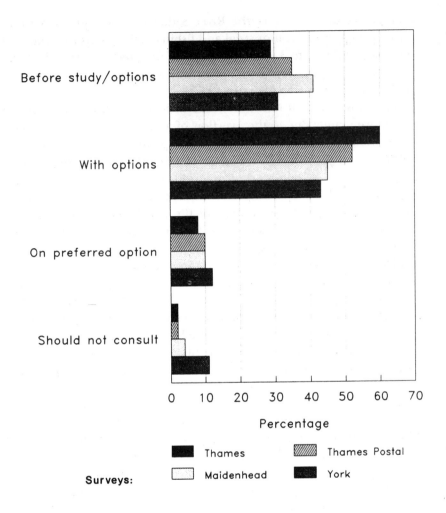

Figure 7.3: Preferences for consultation: public perception of rivers and flood defence research project 1988–94.

Selection of the case study

One of the most seriously affected areas during the severe 1967 and 1983 flood events in the metropolitan area of Lisbon was Setúbal. This is a town with 90,000 inhabitants, located 35 km south of Lisbon, adjacent to the estuary of the River Sado. It is a fast-growing town, based primarily on its industrial and fishing activities, its harbour and also its proximity to Lisbon. Its process of growth is typical of the development of metropolitan areas, rather than of the medium-sized towns it now comprises (Saraiva 1987).

The most severe floods that occur in Setúbal (DGO 1985, DGRN 1989) are mainly due to the overflow of a small creek named Ribeira do Livramento. This creek may be completely dry during summer periods, and yet reach a discharge of 123 m³/sec for a flood event with an estimated 100-year return period (LNEC 1986). Its ephemeral nature, typical of many southern European rivers, has implications both for the public's perception of the risk it represents and their attitudes to its management. The final downstream reach was culverted under the developing town at the beginning of this century, and this has meant that run-off conditions are made more difficult owing to tidal conditions drowning out the river's outflow to the sea.

After the major 1983 floods, the local authorities initiated hydrological studies. The flood regime was characterised, with the estimation of different variables – such as the hydrographs corresponding to several return periods and the probable maximum flood. In addition, the hydraulic conditions of the flows, the sediment transport and estimation of flood volumes were assessed (LNEC 1986). Areas likely to be subject to inundation were estimated and mapped.

Several neighbourhoods, both modern and old, are affected by flooding. In the older areas it is common to see individual flood proofing measures such as permanent or replaceable flood boards protecting the doorways of shops and houses. This type of measure has also been incorporated in some new buildings to protect basements and parking spaces.

The major flood events of 1967 and 1983 were caused by extreme flows exceeding the channel capacity so that the river came out of its banks. Some relatively minor flooding occurs almost annually, affecting certain areas in the lowest part of the town, and this is due to deficiencies in the urban drainage system. Therefore residents and shop owners are, to some extent, familiar with this type of hazard.

Setúbal has been developing along the main valley and flood plain. High grade agricultural soils have been built upon, which has increased the imperviousness of the catchment and now forms a significant reason for the increased flood risk. Certain powerful interest groups at a local level have much to gain from fast urban growth and appear to be unenthusiastic about a planned approach to development. Local authorities have been sensitive to the wishes of these interest groups and have adopted a 'permissive' attitude towards developers and builders. However, some relatively newly formed environmental groups have promoted campaigns against flood plain development and encroachment. Alternative plans have been suggested, incorporating development control and the preservation of the flood plain as a natural park area.

At the time the municipal master plan for Setúbal was being prepared and discussed, an important set of biophysical, social and economic data was collected. The availability of this data then required efficient decision support systems, adequate for both land use planning and flood plain management. These circumstances were crucial in the decision to adopt Setúbal as a relevant and comprehensive case study. The purpose was to select an area that could be representative of the main problems affecting a southern European urban district and locations vulnerable to flood hazards. The existence of different groups within the public with recent experience of flood events was also one of the reasons for this choice.

Public perception of flood risks
Several factors contribute to the perception of a given risk (Lima 1989, Fordham 1992, Emery 1986) such as the physical characteristics of the hazard (frequency, proximity, the possibility of forecast, possibility of human control), socio-economic status, cultural background, previous flood experience and individual characteristics such as age, educational level and underlying value orientations. Furthermore, perception varies with the type of groups involved. As has been noted above, in this respect the general public and experts do not perceive the meaning and intensity of a specific risk – nor its solution – in the same way (Fordham 1992).

In the Setúbal study the following five factors were hypothesised to contribute to the perception of natural hazards. First, there is the importance of previous flood experience. Both residents and shop owners were divided into two groups: those with and those without experience of flood events. Secondly, we wished to explore the influence of educational level. Two groups of residents were considered: one with medium/high and one with low educational achievement levels. However, it – interestingly – proved impossible to select a sample of residents with medium/high educational achievement level because none lived on the ground floor and thus none had ever been directly affected by floods (as defined in the study).

Thirdly, the difference between the perception of different types of people affected in the flood plain was explored, specifically the residents and shop owners. The perception of different types of people involved in the problem was also explored: people directly affected in the flood plain and professionals or local authority members. Finally, the identification of possible cultural adaptations to the flood occurrence and their importance in the perception of flood hazards were targeted. To this end a social survey using structured interviews was carried out in Setúbal, examining flood risk perception, causal attribution and patterns of flood event induced action. All the additional information that was provided by respondents during the lengthy interviews was tape recorded and transcribed.

Sample and questionnaire design

Different categories of the public were analysed. People affected in the flood plain – such as residents and shop owners located at ground floor level in the Ribeira do Livramento flood plain – were selected. These groups were divided according to a control criterion, namely by previous personal experience of a major flood event. The professional and technical staff of the municipality were also sampled, as were the decision makers (local authority members: the president of the municipality and members of the executive board).

The chosen sample comprised sixty residents and sixty shop owners; sixteen professionals and all the local authorities – namely seven members of the executive board and the president of the municipality. The sub-groups examined in the survey are shown in Figure 7.4.

The questionnaire and the interviews were structured according to the following topics. First, we asked for socio-demographic data: age, marital status, educational level, occupational status, residential history, and residential ownership. Secondly, we used questions to elicit attitudes toward the neighbourhood and perception of 'the local problems' to be solved. The subjects were asked to talk about their neighbourhood, their level of attachment to it and the reasons for this attachment. Afterwards they were asked to identify the major

Figure 7.4: Segments of the population considered in the case study.

local problems to be solved as well as the obstacles preventing the solution of these problems. Their personal involvement in any kind of action for finding or implementing possible solutions to the existing problems was also examined.

Thirdly, flood hazard experience was quantified. The residents were asked about their personal knowledge of flood hazards in the area and if they had any personal experience of having their houses flooded. They were also asked about their perception of the major flood in 1983 and the possibility that such an event might happen again. Their perception of the damages caused by floods and their personal behaviour during the floods were also examined, including any kind of actions they had undertaken in their residence in order to mitigate the effects of the hazards. The subjects were also asked for their views on what is an appropriate attitude with respect to floods.

A further category of information sought was on causal attribution and environmental participation. The subjects were asked about the causes of floods in Setúbal. Only after being allowed to describe the causes of flood events as they perceive them was the real cause mentioned – that is, the Livramento river – and possible solutions to the problem and potential difficulties were then investigated. Interviewees were then asked about their personal participation in previous initiatives aimed at the solution of the flood problems and the reasons for their specific behaviour. Additionally they were asked for their opinion about how the local population can contribute to the mitigation of flood hazards.

We also broadened our enquiries to look at the perception of other environmental hazards. After the taped, in-depth interviewing, respondents were asked to consider a list of fourteen environmental hazards and to assess them in several dimensions, using a 5-point Lickert scale. Both natural hazards, such as floods and earthquakes; and anthropogenic hazards, such as car accidents and air pollution, were mentioned. Respondents were asked to rate the extent to which such hazards affect people in general or affect them personally, and the extent to which such hazards affect people at the local, national, European and global levels. Finally, they were asked to evaluate the extent to which these hazards can have a solution and who is in the best position to solve them: namely, international agencies and agreements, national governments, local authorities or local populations, or whether they think that no one can really solve such complex problems.

The fieldwork data collection
The interviews were carried out during 1992 and early 1993 and were designed to last from thirty to sixty minutes, but since most of the questions were open ended no time limit was imposed on the respondents and the actual duration was between thirty minutes and two hours. The interviews (which were tape recorded in order to carry out a content analysis of the verbal responses) were conducted with a structured questionnaire, but this contained some 'open' questions which provided opportunities for respondents to comment in their own words. Furthermore, interviewers were encouraged to note down any additional comments that were made during the lengthy interviews. A total of eighty-one interviews was completed. The distribution among different groups of residents and shop owners is presented in Tables 7.1 and 7.2.

The response to the survey was good in the sense that most of the respondents became very interested and involved in the issues under discussion. However, it was impossible to interview all the potential respondents. In the group of residents, four were unable to answer, twelve could not be contacted and five refused to participate. In the group of shop owners, fourteen could not be contacted and four refused to participate. In the group of professionals, three did not answer. All the seven members of the executive board responded to the survey and only the president was not interviewed, owing to timetabling difficulties.

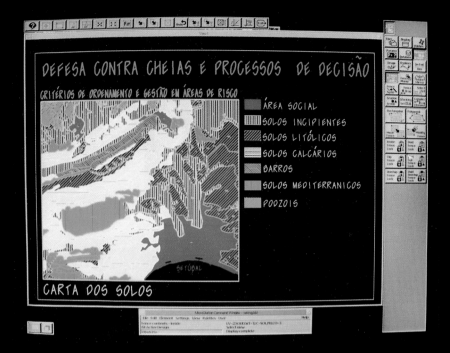

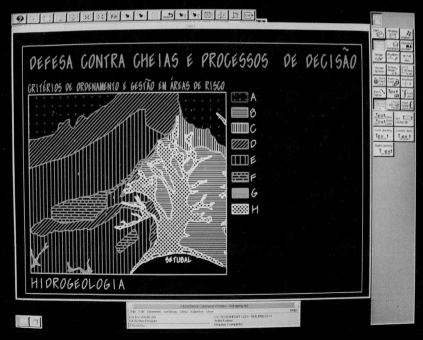

Figure 7.6: Some results provided by GIS.

LEFT: *The Setúbal flood plain showing recent flood plain development and the culverting of the Livramento river.*

BELOW: *Setúbal showing development pressures in the alluvial plain.*

RIGHT: *Individual methods of flood control: a permanent flood board across a residential doorway in the older part of the town.*

BELOW: *Individual methods of flood control: a removable flood board across a commercial doorway in the older part of the town.*

LEFT: *The Livramento river, Setúbal.*

BELOW: *Individual methods of flood control: permanent flood boards across residential doorways in the older part of the town.*

Table 7.1: Sample distribution of residents and shop owners.

	Residents	Shop owners	Total
With flood experience	22	22	44
Without flood experience	17	20	37
	39	42	81

Table 7.2: Sample distribution of technicians and local authorities.

	Total
Technicians	13
Local authorities	7

The GIS data needs

In this case study two different GIS (Intergraph and IDRISI) were used to take advantage of the specific tools and utilities available in each of them, and to enhance the quality of the processes involved. The drawback in using different systems is with the data transfer. Many transfer formats had to be tried before the most suitable format was adopted, insuring data integrity and avoiding data or data structure losses.

As a preliminary task, the existing cartography was digitised. Information such as aerial photographs and other images was also digitised, in a raster format with a scanner. However, most of the cartography – the purely graphic information – was digitised through CAD-like software; other software packages provided a data validation process.

With a GIS it is possible to produce new information by taking advantage of existing algorithms. The production of new maps, such as slope or elevation maps, must be preceded by using a digital terrain model (DTM). This process was undertaken for the whole catchment.

Hydrologic and hydraulic modelling

This case study did not neglect the actual flooding itself, to compare with the public perceptions.

In order to have an approximate knowledge of the discharge values in a particular cross-section of a river, a hydrologic model was used.

This model relates precipitation to discharge, considering parameters that characterise both the relevant meteorological event and the river catchment basin – such as rainfall distribution, soil properties, soil cover and other human-related activities including land use.

The relationship between river flow discharges and water depths is then characterised by hydraulic modelling. In this case the river characterisation is a main factor. Mathematical modelling of hydraulic phenomena is labour intensive in terms of both human effort and computer power, but the GIS provides a good basis for implementing hydrologic and hydraulic models, taking advantage of all data directly available in the system and providing scenarios of flood hazards for different flood alleviation measures.

The methodology used in the hydrologic and hydraulic characterisation of the risk areas is presented in Table 7.3. The objective was to define the flood-affected areas, using relevant input data such as precipitation and land use. The application of a rainfall-runoff model was necessary to determine flood hydrographs, and maximum floods used in the hydraulic model were necessary to define the flood-prone areas. First, the hydrologic model XSRAIN (Verdin and Morel-Seytoux 1981) was used. In this model, the estimation of rainfall-runoff relations in ungauged watersheds is made with a correspondence established between the Soil Conservation Service curve number (a run-off index calibrated against soil-land cover complexes) and hydraulic soil parameters appearing in modern physically-based infiltration equations.

Program XSRAIN can generate a flood hydrograph for a given rainfall event, and to use this model it is necessary to consider various types of data such as basin data (watershed limit, area, slope and length of the principal watercourse), curve number (a function of the land use and geological characteristics) and rainfall data, based on historic records or design values. Other data necessary to run the hydrologic model are selected and entered by the user. These data are the Huff quartile time distribution of storm hyetographs and the time step for flood hydrograph computation.

The second step in defining the flood-affected areas is to run a hydraulic model whose output is the calculation of backwater profiles, and here the HEC-2 model for computing water surface profiles was used. This model allows the calculation and graphical representation of backwater profiles for steady flow conditions. Supercritical or

Table 7.3: The methodology used in the hydrological and hydraulic characterisation.

USER	Operating system UNIX	GIS
Input ➡	*Hydrologic model* (rainfall-runoff model) ⬇	Input ⬅
Input ➡	Hydrographs and maximum flood ⬇ *Hydraulic model* (calculation of backwater profiles) ⬇ Flood planning modelling ➡	Cartography 1/2000 ⬅ *Images with flood hazard areas*

subcritical flows in natural or lined cross-sections for several flow rates can be considered with or without singularities such as bridges or levees. To run this program the user must input the identified cross-sections used for calculations, the Manning coefficients of overbanks and channel, and the specification of the type of flow: subcritical or supercritical.

For the output of the hydraulic model various scenarios can be considered with flood-affected areas defined by the use of appropriate data sets. These scenarios can be based upon different return periods, different land uses and, eventually, different structural measures to control floods. Implementing an existing model in the framework of a GIS allows the integration of information from different sources and of different types and adds significantly to the quality of the resulting output.

THE SETÚBAL CASE STUDY: SELECTED RESEARCH RESULTS

Public perception of the hazard
The findings from the questionnaire survey show a widespread perception of the flood situation in Setúbal. All those interviewed were

capable of describing, locating and identifying the causes of flood events correctly. The Setúbal flood problem is as old as human settlement in this area itself. The flooding which occurred during the eighteenth century was of such importance that it was described in local literature (Ramos 1992).

All the respondents correctly attributed the flood problem in Setúbal to multiple causes. Content analysis of the responses enabled the classification of causes presented in Figure 7.5. All groups understood the flood hazard to be a problem that is partially natural or non-controllable and partially human-made or controllable, in what can be designated as a 'quasi-natural' hazard (Fordham 1992). Several solutions were mentioned that could be implemented to minimise the problem, but respondents realised that even if these solutions were to be implemented, the flood problems would still persist.

The flood hazard literature reveals the importance of experience in the development of flood hazard perception (Kates 1962, Penning-Rowsell 1976, Lave and Lave 1991). In this research the concept of

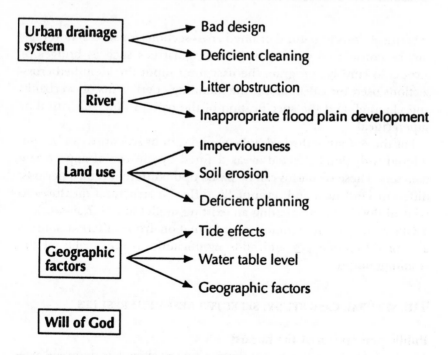

Figure 7.5: Flood causes identified by respondents.

'flood experience' was defined as ever having had a flood inside their houses or shops. However, most of the respondents without flood experience have witnessed a flood situation at least once. Perhaps this explains why it is – contrary to most research results elsewhere – that the group without flood experience recognises, describes and identifies the flood causes in approximately the same way as the respondents with flood experience.

Nevertheless the respondents without flood experience had some difficulty in answering a question concerning the flood frequency: 35 per cent of the residents without flood experience and 50 per cent of the shop owners without flood experience answered 'I don't know', and had a more optimistic opinion about the likelihood of another flood in the future.

The different reactions of different groups
As indicated above, different groups were sampled; in natural hazard events different segments of the public are involved in the process (Correia *et al.* 1990). The literature has shown that researchers have taken a particular interest in studying the flood risk perception of different groups of the population involved, particularly between the public affected and the professionals involved in the design of flood alleviation schemes (Green *et al.* 1991, Fordham 1992). Different groups have distinct perspectives on the problem and, consequently, have diverse and conflicting expectations of appropriate and likely behaviour before and during a flood event. Conflict may also occur when considering the solution to the flood problem. Therefore, there is a need to understand the different perceptions of the public in order to arrive at adequate flood alleviation measures – in terms of both structural and non-structural solutions – incorporating the specific views of the population (Caude 1988).

In our research the residents and shop owners appear to have a more optimistic view about the likelihood of another major flood than do the professionals and local authority members. In terms of severity, the local authority politicians consider the flood in Setúbal less important as a problem. However, the different groups describe the situation, damages, responsibilities and action during hazards in the same way. The population at large is not aware of the civil protection service as an agency with responsibilities for providing help during hazard situations.

In terms of cause identification, some differences can be observed among and between groups. The cumulative impact of an inadequate urban drainage system and tidal effects were easily identified by residents and shop owners and referred to as the most common cause of flood events. The professionals have a broader view of the situation and mention not only the deficiencies in urban drainage and tide effects but also the land use problems and the water table levels. This is a more 'scientific' point of view that is perhaps more difficult for the general population to grasp (Lima 1993).

The local authority members perceive a combination of causes that can be considered as somewhat intermediate between the perceptions of the general population and the perceptions of the professionals. They mention the joint effect of inappropriate urban drainage, the tidal effects and the imperviousness of some areas of the watershed.

Political affiliations among local authority members appear to have some influence on opinions about flood risk. The members of the executive board belonging to the political party with a majority in local government had a more optimistic view about the likelihood of a future big flood. This group emphasised the importance of aspects of the geographical location: Setúbal is built in an area where floods occur. While this is a human-made cause, the origin is very remote and thus no responsibility can accrue to them. The political opposition emphasised the increasing imperviousness of the watershed. In considering the lack of solutions to the problem, the group of politicians of the majority party referred to external reasons, such as lack of funds or the many complexities of the problem. The opposition referred to more local and tangible reasons, such as the lack of political will in controlling development or countering the hazard.

It is generally understood that 'disaster sub-cultures' exist as groups in society (Wenger 1978). These are a cultural response in communities that are frequently exposed to a given type of threat (Moore 1964, Wenger and Weller 1978, Quarantelli 1985, Laska 1990, Fordham 1992) such as is apparent in populations that have been living for long periods in flood plains. Within these sub-cultures, emergency situations are faced with less panic and many spontaneous measures are adopted in order to mitigate against the consequences of flood hazards.

In our residents' group, perhaps because of the frequency and the long history of the floods, we found collective action patterns and cognitive patterns related to adjustment to the hazard situation, as described by Kates (1978). As mentioned above, many householders have installed flood boards at the threshold to protect their homes from the flood waters. Another form of adjustment is knowledge of the tidal influence; this is a form of cognitive adjustment through the elimination of doubt, thus making the situation predictable.

In the group of shop owners with flood experience it is possible to identify two different kinds of behaviour. Among shop owners with frequent flood experience there exists a group that shows the same flood mitigation characteristics as the resident group; that is, the use of flood boards and the checking of tide levels. Those shop owners at risk from infrequent floods (such as occurred in 1983) adopt measures that reduce but do not prevent damages (such as obtaining insurance) or they do not adopt any type of protection; in rare but severe flood events they can experience serious problems.

Most respondents had not been active in seeking a solution to the problem. However, it is interesting to note that a significant number of people believed that something or even much could be achieved if the general public took a more active role. The professionals and politicians emphasise the importance of technical solutions in the resolution of the problem. The public see flood control as a responsibility of the municipality. They perceive their role as a civic one, to put pressure on the municipality. Some research has shown that the perceived controllability of the hazard increases public participation (Rochford and Blocker 1991), although this has not been found to be the case in Setúbal.

The European Community Directive 85/337/EEC makes public participation a legal requirement in European member states for some specific situations. However, in Portugal there is little evidence of a culture of public participation other than as a contingent response during and immediately following severe flood events. But this case study emphasises the need to understand the public perception of floods and flood hazard management in order to increase the efficiency of possible solutions to the flood problem; in many instances damage from floods will be higher unless the flood-prone react. It will be necessary, however, to develop public awareness through the implementation of a risk communication programme (Slovic 1986, Keeney and Winterfeldt 1986, Handmer and Penning-Rowsell 1990). One possible tool in this process is the use of GIS.

The Geographic Information System

The main result of integrating information and modelling in a GIS has been the development of PSIGH (Participação pública com Sistema de Informação Geográfica em problemas Hidráulicos – public participation with geographical information systems on hydraulic problems). This versatile GIS model is aimed at river basin flood hazard assessment and management, and related aspects of land use planning and management. It is being implemented to deliver information to two types of people – namely, the professionals in a decision-making environment and the public in general – in order to facilitate the participation process.

At the current stage of development PSIGH is based on the aggregation of a hydrologic model (XSRAIN) and a hydraulic model (HEC-2) running on and with data supplied by a GIS. Both hydrologic and hydraulic models have been used before in many flood studies in Portugal with good results. PSIGH is using a minimum of ten thematic maps provided by the GIS. The main outputs have been the characterisation of the flooded areas, including the flood discharges in the main channel and flood plains, the depths of flow, the velocity of flow, and consequently the total flood areas and volumes for each flood event. The characterisation of the influence of each hydrological and hydraulic controlling parameter is the output to be shown to the general public against a background of the different land uses, land use plans and human activities of the areas concerned. This necessarily non-technical output is particularly suited to the graphical capabilities of GIS.

Some examples of GIS output are displayed in Figure 7.6 (between pages 178 and 179). In a more advanced version, PSIGH will have real-time modelling capabilities, although this is not yet implemented. Nevertheless, analysis can now be undertaken of historic flood events, or for different flood scenarios. Flood zones can be identified and the safety of people and property can be assessed in relation to flood depths generated. At a later stage, a flood damage model will be appended to allow a systematic comparison of the economic merit of alternative flood alleviation measures, with full GIS facilities.

REFINING OUR INTEGRATED CONCEPTUAL MODEL FOR FLOOD HAZARD ASSESSMENT AND MANAGEMENT

The progress of our research programme has highlighted the need for a conceptual model to integrate the many components and aspects that were considered – public perception, GIS, hydrologic and hydraulic modelling, public participation – and give coherence to this diversified approach.

Figure 7.7 presents a refined conceptual model developed for this purpose. It includes five basic phases of flood hazard management; namely, data collection, analysis, synthesis, assessment and decision making (see also Figure 4.1). While decision making has been isolated here as the final phase, it is recognised that decision making will occur throughout the process and it should be understood that this should incorporate public participation.

In the first phase, a digital database for the catchment is implemented, collecting and storing different types of data – such as biophysical, socio-economic and perception data. Following this, the main components of the data are analysed in order to select the key variables for assessing the general situation of the catchment and the flood plain in terms of biophysical and regulatory issues, hydrological and hydraulic regimes and variables, socio-economic assessment and the characterisation of perception patterns and causal effects.

The third phase allows for the generation of a comprehensive synthesis of the catchment characteristics and for the integration of specific components in the flood plain risk areas. This corresponds to the current stage of the research discussed here, where public perception of flood risks from residents, shop owners, local authority politicians and professionals have been analysed jointly with the physical and human processes that contribute to the current and future increase of flood risk and vulnerability in the catchment.

The subsequent two steps lead directly to the decision-making process in flood plain management. They incorporate the development of scenario generation and the assessment of the impacts of those scenarios on flood effects and flood perceptions. The scenario formulation will be based on urban development patterns and on different options for flood alleviation measures. Four options can be considered in general terms. There is, first, the 'do nothing' option, which assumes that urban development will grow, as in former

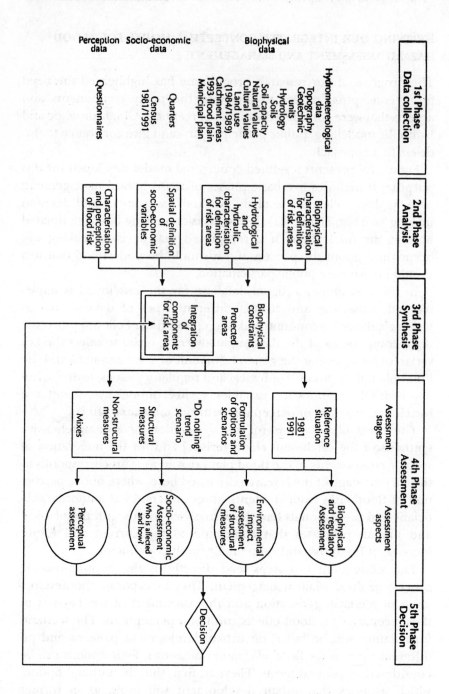

Figure 7.7: Conceptual model for flood hazard analysis and management.

decades, with few constraints and that no structural or non-structural measures will be implemented. The second option is the structural option: incorporating measures for flood control such as building a dam in the catchment headwaters and retention basins in the flood plain inside the city. The third possible choice is the non-structural option: the application of flood plain regulation, zoning and regulatory constraints within the catchment, through the application of environmental protection regulations. A fourth option would be the use of a mix of structural and non-structural measures.

For each of these scenarios, an assessment process can be generated using the GIS capabilities. This process will include a comprehensive approach, integrating the main components that have been developed throughout the research. A multi-attribute assessment of perception and socio-economic trends, and the environmental effects of the different types of measures, could be identified and tested. This process could be a useful tool to support decision making at the local level and facilitate the assessment and monitoring of the process within a comprehensive context. The graphical display abilities of the GIS are an important element in the efficient communication of information to the public, especially when this information is sometimes – and inevitably – highly technical (Bernardo *et al.* 1993).

CONCLUSIONS AND POLICY IMPLICATIONS

The innovative case study described here has examined a complex decision-making area comprising communities with a traditional flood culture in close proximity to new residents lacking flood experience. It demonstrates the complexity of flood plain resource management which can result in conflicting preferences for flood plain uses: for economic development, heritage value, ecological significance and, importantly, flood storage. It has underlined the importance, in the decision-making process, of the availability of adequate information to as many of the interested parties as possible, and in an easily accessible form. Finally, it has suggested a refined model for the integration of these varied components into a system that is technically, socially and ecologically acceptable.

A number of major conclusions and policy implications arise from the research discussed above. First and foremost we must emphasise again that flood plain management programmes cannot be dissociated from catchment land use management, and thus an integrated approach in this respect needs to prevail. Also, planning for flood alleviation requires a mix of technical, social, economic and environmental concerns and solutions. There is a need to take into account multi-dimensional problems, multi-disciplinary solutions, a wide range of tools and a complex and multi-directional (vertical and horizontal) institutional framework. Our study reinforces the point that accurate flood frequency analysis and hydraulic modelling are essential tools for the definition of areas subject to inundation and for the assessment of flood risk. Appropriate GIS are also useful and powerful tools, not only for flood plain management, but also for facilitating the dialogue with decision makers, interest groups and the public in general.

As stressed elsewhere, a combination of structural and non-structural approaches to flood plain management should be based upon and reflect the local context and its physical and social conditions. In this respect the interface with the public plays an important role in flood plain management. The examination of public perceptions and attitudes to the flood hazard is an essential means of understanding how the public copes with those events now and how to influence the planning of future relief, emergency and recovery measures.

Finally, the case study re-emphasises the view that local level responses and the local context are key factors in a proactive hazard management process. To this end environmental concerns should be combined with flood plain management at all stages. Comprehensive land use planning and resource management in the whole catchment, the protection of natural and cultural values of flood plains and rivers, and the proper consideration of environmental impacts of structural and non-structural management choices are important aspects, all requiring appropriate analysis and consideration. The methodology described here is still being developed for application in other southern European countries, and its further refinement will be pursued in future research.

REFERENCES

Bernardo, F.; Ramos, I.; Saraiva, M.G. and Correia, F.N. (1993) *Sistemas de Informação Geográfica no Ordenamento de Áreas de Risco de Cheias*. II ESIG93. Caso de Setúbal. Estoril, Portugal

Caude, G. (1988) *L'inondation des villes, un Phénomène Maîtisable?* Les annales de la

Recherche Urbaine. Paris, France: Dunod 40

Correia, F.N.; Saraiva, M.G. and Soczka, L. (1992) *Coping with Floods in Setúbal: a few steps towards an integrated approach.* Paper presented at NATO Advanced Studies Institute seminar 'Coping with Floods', Erice, Italy

Correia, F.N.; Saraiva, M.G.; Soczka, L. and Soeiro, C. (1990) *Public Perception and Public Participation in Water Projects.* European Conference of Water Management. Paris, France: Commission of the European Communities and French Ministry of Environment

Cotgrove, S. (1982) *Catastrophe or Cornucopia.* Chichester, UK: John Wiley and Sons

Craik, K.H. (1970) The Environmental Dispositions of Environmental Decision-Makers. *The Annals of the American Academy of Political and Social Science: society and its physical environment,* 389, 87–94

DGO (1985) *Estudo das Causas das Cheias na Região de Lisboa. Relatório Síntese. Bacia Hidrográfica da Ribeira da Laje* (Study of Flood Causes in Lisbon Region. Synthesis Report. Ribeira da Laje Riverbasin). Lisbon, Portugal: MPAT, SEALOT

DGRN (1989) *Estudo das Causas das Cheias na Região de Lisboa. Relatório Síntese. Bacia Hidrográfica do Rio de Loures e Ribeira de Odivelas* (Study of Flood Causes in Lisbon Region. Synthesis Report. Rio de Loures e Ribeira de Odivelas River Basins). Lisbon, Portugal: MPAT, SEARN

ECON (1993) *The River Restoration Project, Phase 1: the feasibility study.* Report to the River Restoration Project. Norwich, UK: University of East Anglia

Emery, J. (1986) *Disaster, Distress, Disease.* London, UK: Middlesex University, Flood Hazard Research Centre

Fordham, M.H. (1992) *Choice and Constraints in Flood Hazard Mitigation: the environmental attitudes of floodplain residents and engineers.* Unpublished PhD thesis. London, UK: Middlesex University

Fordham, M.H. (1993) Valuing the environment: the attitudes of flood plain residents and flood defence engineers. *Proceedings of the Values and the Environment Conference,* 163–69. University of Surrey

Gardiner, J.L. (1988) Environmentally Sensitive River Engineering: examples from the Thames catchment. In Petts, G. (ed.) *Regulated Rivers: research and management,* vol. 2. Chichester, UK: John Wiley and Sons

Gardiner, J.L. (1991) *Influences on the Development of River Catchment Planning in the Thames Basin.* Unpublished PhD thesis. Southampton, UK: University of Southampton

Green, C.H.; Tunstall, S.M. and Fordham, M.H. (1991) The Risks from Flooding: which risks and whose perception? *Disasters,* 15 (3), 227–36

Handmer, J.W. and Penning-Rowsell, E.C. (eds) (1990) *Hazards and the Communication of Risk.* Aldershot, UK: Gower Technical Press

Kates, R.W. (1962) *Hazard and Choice Perception in Flood Plain Management.* Department of Geography Research Paper 78. Chicago, USA: University of Chicago

Kates, R.W. (1978) *Risk Assessment of Environmental Hazard.* Chichester, UK: John Wiley and Sons

Keeney, R.L. and Winterfeldt, D.V. (1986) Improving Risk Communication. *Risk Analysis,* 6 (4), 417–24

Laska, S.B. (1990) Homeowner Adaption to Flooding: an application of the general hazards coping theory. *Environment and Behaviour*, 22 (3), 320–57

Lave, T.R. and Lave, L.B. (1991) Public Perception of the Risks of Floods: implications for communication. *Risk Analysis*, 2 (2), 255–67

Lima, L. (1989) *Contributos para o Estudo da representação do Risco*. Lisbon, Portugal: LNEC

Lima, M.L. (1993) *Percepção de Riscos Ambientais: Representações e Identidades Sociais*. Comunicação no I Colóquio de 'Ambiente': 4, Educação e Política Ambientais. Lisbon, Portugal: ISPA

LNEC (1986) *Estudo Hidrológico e Hidráulico das Cheias e Inundações na Cidade de Setúbal* (Hydrologic and Hydraulic Study of Floods in the Town of Setúbal). Relatórios 245 e 246/86. Lisbon, Portugal: NHHF

Moore, H.E. (1964) *And the Winds Blew*. Austin, Texas, USA: University of Texas

Penning-Rowsell, E.C. (1976) The Effect of Flood Damage on Land Use Planning. *Geographica Polonica*, 34, 139–53

Quarantelli, F. (1985) What is a Disaster: the need for clarification in definition and conceptualization in research. In Sowder, B. (ed.) *Disasters and Mental Health*. Washington DC, USA: National Institute of Mental Health

Ramos, I. (1992) *As Quintas Envolventes de Setúbal*. Uma Proposta de Ordenamento. Final Report for the Degree of Landscape Architecture. Lisbon, Portugal: ISA

Rochford, E.B. and Blocker, T.J. (1991) Coping with 'Natural' Hazards as Stressor: the predictor of activism in a flood disaster. *Environment and Behaviour*, 23 (2)

Saraiva, M. da G. (1987) *A Defesa contra Cheias e sua Inserção no Ordenamento do Território. Area Metropolitana de Lisboa* (Flood Defence and Land Use Planning. Lisbon Metropolitan area). MSc thesis in Urban and Regional Planning. Lisbon, Portugal: UTL

Saraiva, M. da G.; Pinto, P.; Rabaca, J.; Ramos, A. and Revez, M. (1992) *Protection, Reclamation and Improvement of Small Watercourses in the Suburbs of Evora, Portugal*. Paper given at the international symposium 'The Ecological Basis for River Management', Leicester, UK

Sewell, W.R.D. (1971) Environmental Perceptions and Attitudes of Engineers and Public Health Officials. *Environment and Behaviour*, March, 23–59

Sewell, W.R.D. (1974) The Role of Perceptions of Professionals in Environmental Decision Making. In Coppock, J.T. and Wilson, C.B. (eds), *Environmental Quality*, 109–31. Edinburgh, UK: Scottish Academic Press

Sewell, W.R.D. and Little, B.R. (1973) Specialists, Laymen and the Process of Environmental Appraisal. *Regional Studies*, 7, 161–71

Slovic, P. (1986) Informing and Educating the Public about Risk. *Risk Analysis*, 6 (4), 403–15

Tapsell, S.M.; Fordham, M.; Tunstall, S.M. and Horne, M. (1991) *The River Environment and You – Postal Survey: Datchet to Walton Bridge*. Draft Final Report. London, UK: Middlesex University, Flood Hazard Research Centre

Tunstall, S. and Fordham, M. (1990) *Thames Perception and Attitude Survey – Datchet to Walton Bridge*. Draft Final Report. London, UK: Middlesex University, Flood Hazard Research Centre

Verdin and Morel-Seytoux (1981) *User's Manual for XSRAIN – a Fortran IV Programme for Calculation of Flood Hydrografics for Ungaged Watershed.* Federal Highway Administration. Washington DC, USA

Wenger, D.E. (1978) Community Response to Disaster: functional and structural alterations. In Quarantelli, E.L. (ed.) *Disasters, Theory and Research.* Beverly Hills, California, USA: Sage Publications Inc.

Wenger, D.E. and Weller, J.M. (1978) *Disaster Subcultures: the cultural residues of community disasters.* Disaster Research Center Paper 9. Columbus, Ohio, USA

White, G.F. (1966a) Formation and Role of Public Attitudes. In Jarett, H. (ed.) *Environmental Quality in a Growing Economy.* Baltimore, USA: Johns Hopkins Press

White, G.F. (1966b) Optimal Flood Damage Management. In Kneese, A.V. and Smith, S.C. (eds) *Water Research*, 251–69. Baltimore, USA: Johns Hopkins Press for Resources for the Future

CHAPTER 8

Flood Hazard Assessment, Modelling and Management: Future Directions

Edmund Penning-Rowsell and Maureen Fordham

SYNTHESIS

This volume has considered a number of aspects of flood hazard assessment, modelling and management, and each chapter has drawn conclusions about its particular specialist area.

Thus, in Chapter 2, we draw the conclusion that the current information about the potential for climate change is not conclusive, and that the pace of climate change identified by the current information does not indicate the need for 'panic' responses. All the information suggests that global climates are warming, and that sea-level rise can be anticipated. Nevertheless, the pace of such sea-level rise, in so far as information is currently adequate, is not such that governments and policy makers need to make decisions that they might regret in the future.

The same conclusion is confirmed by more detailed results in Chapter 5. Here the case study of the Netherlands indicates that the pace of sea-level rise is such that there is sufficient time to make decisions on the basis of better information to be obtained in the future. In addition, the pace of sea-level rise as currently investigated is not such as to mean that the necessary investment in dike-raising is unmanageable or indeed not worthwhile. The information coming from the ISOS model indicates that the benefits of further dike-raising, either now or in the future, far outweigh the costs likely to be incurred. This conclusion appears to be sound irrespective of the uncertainties concerning gauging the full impacts of flooding.

These full impacts of flooding have further been discussed in Chapter 3. That chapter concluded that more attention needs to be given to gauging some of the impacts of flooding that have hitherto been regarded as 'intangibles'. A comprehensive conceptual model of full flood impacts indicates that these can dominate in certain circumstances, and empirical information from a large survey confirms earlier suggestions that those vulnerable to flooding consider that the hitherto unquantified aspects and impacts of floods are those that are most significant.

The survey results also give insight into the effectiveness of intervention and coping strategies. The results show that good flood warnings are effective, in most circumstances, and that social support for flood victims is important in reducing stress levels. Whilst the damage to contents and household structure is important, this is not the primary factor that contributes to the flood victim's judgement as to the overall severity of flood events. That severity is linked more to the dislocation and disruption caused by flooding, and this can be ameliorated by social support and flood warnings.

In Chapter 4 we have concluded that the regional scale analysis of flood impacts is the area most neglected in hazard modelling to date. This is mainly because of the errors necessarily involved in such regional scale analysis, which hitherto have been difficult to quantify. The German case study indicates an innovative approach to using secondary source data as inputs to the flood hazard assessment model, whilst still stressing the importance of topography and flood frequency. The case study also indicates the large magnitude of potential losses from flooding in that area in relation to the budgets available for flood alleviation schemes.

In Chapters 6 and 7 we have evaluated different policy responses to hazards, as part of the management of those hazards in an integrated manner. The research into flood warning systems indicates that there is potential for transferring good practices across the countries of the European Union, particularly in respect of communication methods and technology. On the other hand, the research indicates that little is known about end-user satisfaction and response to flood warnings, and this is obviously a gap in our knowledge. We need, through these and other ways, to monitor the effectiveness of flood warning systems, in terms of both technical and customer satisfaction.

Our reports of research results finish with information on the interface with the public, presented in Chapter 7. The conclusion here, from both the theoretical discussion and the case study information from Portugal and the United Kingdom, suggests that a complex web of interactions affects the way that the public perceives floods and flood alleviation schemes. On the one hand, the public can readily understand the nature of flooding if the water courses and the river corridors are adjacent to their properties. On the other hand, those distant from rivers and inexperienced with regard to floods are often taken by surprise when serious events occur. The Portuguese results point to the contrast of perceptions between those living near the flooding and the politicians responsible for decision making. Some of these decision makers appear not to be too concerned about the nature of the hazard, or to wish to minimise its importance; whereas others more readily recognise the change in nature of the catchment involved and the threats that are posed. All in all, an analysis of these different perceptions is shown to be important as an ingredient in understanding the nature of flood hazards and influencing the way in which decisions are made about flood alleviation schemes.

All the information reported in the different chapters of this volume is interconnected. Information on the nature of the hazard should inform policy response, which in turn should be informed by public perceptions and attitudes. Environmental values can be disturbed by ill-designed flood alleviation works, and incorporating such values into decision making is as important as measuring the intangible direct impacts of floods, as has been common in the past. This interconnectedness of all the variables concerned points, of course, to the need for an integrated approach to flood hazard assessment, modelling and management.

POLICY ASSESSMENT: CONTINUING PROBLEMS

From our research on European flood hazards, we can see a number of circumstances in which an integrated approach is being taken and in which results are favourable. This particularly applies to flood hazard management in the Netherlands, where the 1953 flood and the subsequent legislation have put this issue at the top of the national agenda.

In other situations progress has not been so satisfactory. Our research on flood hazard assessment, using case studies reported here and elsewhere (EUROflood Project 1992, 1993), indicates that urban development in flood-prone areas remains a problem. We find too many examples of houses, shops, factories and other buildings continuing to be planned and located in areas of risk, either in ignorance of the hazard that is being created or owing to an expectation that flood protection will be provided. Instances can be cited in Portugal, France, the United Kingdom and Germany, which all indicate a failure of communication between planning authorities and water authorities in this respect. We recognise the difficulty of decisions about this kind of development, and do not regard the flood plain as sacrosanct and undevelopable. Nevertheless, the potential impacts of development need to be assessed when decisions are made and, if development occurs, appropriate warning systems and evacuation plans need to be put in place so that the impacts of floods when they come will be minimised.

Secondly, we can see from our research reported both here and elsewhere (EUROflood Project 1993) that flood warning systems remain poorly targeted in many areas. It is often the case that warnings are given indiscriminately, and this can lead to scepticism amongst the public about whether they reflect reality and whether floods are in fact imminent. In certain countries the institutional framework for flood forecasting and warning is excessively complex, and in some instances inappropriate institutions are employed. When warnings are to be given to the public, then messages should be clear, lines of communication should be as direct as possible, and advice as to response should be given. Only in this way will warning effectiveness be maximised.

Decision making is imperfect in the flood hazard management field, resting as it does upon either arbitrary standards or the inadequate totalling of the full impacts of floods on vulnerable populations. We cannot emphasise too strongly the need for decision makers to obtain better information on these impacts, and on the effects of their policies, measures and plans. Particular attention should be given to vulnerable groups within the population – particularly the old and infirm – since our research indicates quite clearly that these are disproportionately affected by floods and the stress and disruption that they bring.

In all this policy development, it is important for governments and local authorities to recognise the need to involve a large number of agencies. Traditionally, flood alleviation policy has been the concern of public works departments, agriculture departments and environment departments, but it is equally clear that social services departments and interior departments should also be involved. These latter institutions are generally the focus of responsibility for emergency planning and relief and this activity needs to be coordinated with the construction-orientated work in other agencies.

FUTURE RESEARCH

As researchers, we naturally look to research to inform policy development. Our research is continuing into European floods in an attempt to fill some of the gaps in our knowledge identified throughout this volume.

We need continually to refine our methods of hazard appraisal and assessment. The detailed investigations of the impacts of floods described in Chapter 3 need to be carried into other sectors of the population and the economy. The nature and extent of these impacts need to be related to a Europe-wide typology of floods, so that policy development in different countries can learn from others by matching response to flood type and other characteristics.

We also need to look further at intervention strategies to counter flood hazards. In particular, we intend to pursue the question of using economic instruments rather than regulatory systems and public investment to reduce our vulnerability to flood hazards. Despite the fact that flood alleviation tends to be regarded as a public good, there may be important instances where economic instruments can deter users from occupying flood-prone areas, or encourage them to take self-financed mitigation actions. This suggests a need for more knowledge about the process of urban encroachment into flood plain areas, and in particular the need to look for best practice in discouraging this urban encroachment through better planning systems and other mechanisms. At the same time, we need to develop our knowledge of the effectiveness of flood warning systems, particularly as they relate to existing unprotected urban development in flood-prone areas, resulting from unwise decisions to locate developments there in the past. This research, we believe, could inform the development of Europe-wide standards for flood warning systems, linked to the developing networks of meteorological forecasting systems across the European Union.

The above research emphasis does not detract from the need to continue to enhance the models we have developed for flood hazard assessment. In particular, regional scale analysis, discussed in Chapter 4, needs further enhancement so that a model can be developed for Europe-wide application. This will necessitate investigating the data sources in different countries that can be used to calibrate this model, and testing the efficiency of the fit between regional scale analysis and local investigations. At the same time, more information is needed on flood damages, since the current databases in different countries are sparse and unevenly distributed.

Finally, further research is needed on the evaluation of flood impacts and decision-making routines. We intend to pursue the enhancement of benefit-cost analysis, discussed in Chapter 3, particularly to involve environmental assets and their evaluation. It is becoming quite apparent that across Europe environmental factors are increasingly important in the management of rivers and coastal zones, and better information about the impacts of floods and flood alleviation measures on these values cannot but improve decision making. At the same time we need to explore ways of integrating such information into decision-making models, which currently are excessively simplistic, concentrating as they do on a narrow view of benefit-cost analysis.

We hope in this way to add rigour to our scientific analysis, and breadth to its scope. Through this, we hope to enhance our understanding of the nature of flood hazards across Europe and gauge their significance. In addition, we look to a degree of standardisation of policies and procedures with regard to decision making concerning investment in flood alleviation and coastal zone management in the European Union countries, based on a common understanding of research needs and outputs. If, through these efforts, our community of researchers contributes to enhancing the cohesion of the European Union, and to better environmental management of its rivers and coastal zones, then some of our objectives will have been met.

REFERENCES

EUROflood Project (1992) *Inception Report*. London, UK: Middlesex University, Flood Hazard Research Centre
EUROflood Project (1993) *First Annual Report*. London, UK: Middlesex University, Flood Hazard Research Centre

Bibliography

Allee, D.J.; Osgood, B.T.; Antle, L.G.; Simpkins, C.E.; Moltz, A.N.; Van der Slice, A. and Westbrook, W.F. (1980) *Human Costs of Flooding and Implementability of Non-structural Damage Reduction in the Tug Fork Valley of West Virginia.* Fort Belvoir, VA, USA: US Army Corps of Engineers

BCEOM (1990) *Dommages de crues (bassins de la Moselle).* Paris, France: BCEOM

Bernardo, F.; Ramos, I.; Saraiva, M.G. and Correia, F.N. (1993) *Sistemas de Informação Geográfica no Ordenamento de Áreas de Risco de Cheias.* II ESIF93. Caso de Setúbal. Estoril, Portugal

Beyene, M. (1992) *Ein Informationssystem für Abschätzung von Hochwasserschadens potentialen* (An Information System for the Estimation of Flood Damage Potentials). Aachen, Germany: Mitteilungen Heft 83 des Instituts für Wasserbau und Wasserwirtschaft der Rheinisch-Westfälischen Technischen Hochschule

Bialas, W.F. and Loucks, D.P. (1978) Nonstructural Flood Plain Planning. *Water Resources Research*, 14 (1), 67–74

Boer, B.; Craig, D.; Handmer, J.W. and Ross, H. (1991) *The Potential Role of Mediation in the Resource Assessment Commission Inquiry Process.* Discussion Paper no. 1. Canberra, Australia: Resource Assessment Commission

Bossman-Aggrey, P.; Parker, D.J. and Green, C.H. (1987) *Dam Safety Management in the United Kingdom.* Middlesex University School of Geography and Planning Paper No. 21. London, UK: Middlesex University, Flood Hazard Research Centre

Buck, W. (1988) *On Improved Flood Control Planning and Analysis of Flood Damage Data.* Paper given at the 39th IEC Meeting of the ICID. Dubrovnik

Burton, I.; Kates, R. and White, G. (1978) *The Environment as Hazard.* New York, USA: Oxford University Press

Caude, G. (1988) *L'inondation des villes, un Phénomène Maîtisable?* Les annales de la Recherche Urbaine. Paris, France: Dunod 40

Chamberlaine, E.R.; Doube, L.; Milne, G.; Rolls, M. and Western, J.S. (1981) *The Experience of Cyclone Tracy.* Canberra, Australia: Australian Government Printing House

Chatterton, J.B. (1994) *EUROflood Country Reports for Germany and the Netherlands.* Internal report to Middlesex University Flood Hazard Research Centre

Chatterton, J.B. and Penning-Rowsell, E.C. (1981) Computer Modelling of Flood Alleviation Benefits. *Proceedings of the American Society of Civil Engineers*, 107 (WR2), 533–47

Church, J.A.; Godfrey, J.S.; Jackett, D.R. and McDougall, T.J. (1991) A Model of Sea Level Rise Caused by Ocean Thermal Expansion. *Journal of Climate,* 4

Cline, W. (1992) *The Economics of Global Warming.* Washington DC, USA: Institute of International Economics

Commissie Rivierdijken (1977) Rapport Commissie Rivierdijken. The Hague, Netherlands: Ministerie van Verkeer en Waterstaat

Correia, F.C. (1987) Multivariate Partial Duration Series in Flood Risk Analysis. In Singh, V.P. (ed.) *Hydrologic Frequency Modelling,* 541–54. New York, USA: Reidel Publishing Company

Correia, F.N.; Saraiva, M.G. and Soczka, L. (1992) *Coping with Floods in Setúbal: a few steps towards an integrated approach.* Paper presented at NATO Advanced Studies Institute seminar 'Coping with Floods', Erice, Italy

Correia, F.N.; Saraiva, M.G.; Soczka, L. and Soeiro, C. (1990) *Public Perception and Public Participation in Water Projects.* European Conference of Water Management. Paris, France: Commission of the European Communities and French Ministry of Environment

Cotgrove, S. (1982) *Catastrophe or Cornucopia.* Chichester, UK: John Wiley and Sons

Council of the European Communities (1992) Council Resolution of 25 February 1992 on the Future Community Policy Concerning the European Coastal Zone (92/C 59/01). *Official Journal of the European Communities,* C 59/1, 6 March

Craik, K.H. (1970) The Environmental Dispositions of Environmental Decision-makers. *The Annals of the American Academy of Political and Social Science: society and its physical environment,* 389, 87–94

Debizet, G. and Caude, G. (1986) *Simulation de dommages en zone urbaine mondiale: application au quartier de Sapiac.* Paris, France: Délégation aux Risques Majeurs

Debo, T.N. and Day, G.N. (1980) Economic Model for Urban Watersheds. *ASCE Journal of the Hydraulics Division,* 15333, 475–87

Delft Hydraulics (1989) *Criteria for Assessing Vulnerability to Sea Level Rise: a global inventory of high risk areas.* Report H838. Delft, Netherlands: Delft Hydraulics

Delft Hydraulics (1989) *Analysis of Vulnerability to the Impacts of Sea Level Rise. A Case Study for the Netherlands.* Delft, Netherlands: Delft Hydraulics

Delft Hydraulics and Rijkswaterstaat (1991) *Impact of Sea Level Rise on Society. A Case Study for the Netherlands.* Delft, Netherlands: Delft Hydraulics and Rijkswaterstaat

Delft Hydraulics and the European American Center for Policy Analysis (EAC/RAND) (1993) *Examination of the Premises of the (Dutch) River Dike Strengthening Program.* Final report, and partial report 2: critical loads. The Hague, Netherlands: Ministerie van Verkeer en Waterstaat

Deutscher Verband für Wasserwirtschaft und Kulturbau (1985) *Ökonomische Bewertung von Hochwasserschutzwirkungen* (Economic Assessment of Flood Mitigating Effects). Bonn, Germany: DVWK-Mitteilungen Heft 10

DGO (1985) *Estudo das Causas das Cheias na Região de Lisboa. Relatório Síntese. Bacia Hidrográfica da Ribeira da Laje* (Study of Flood Causes in Lisbon Region. Synthesis Report. Ribeira da Laje River Basin). Lisbon, Portugal: MPAT, SEALOT

DGRN (1989) *Estudo das Causas das Cheias na Região de Lisboa. Relatório Síntese.*

Bacia Hidrográfica do Rio de Loures e Ribeira de Odivelas (Study of Flood Causes in Lisbon Region. Synthesis Report. Rio de Loures e Ribeira de Odivelas River Basins). Lisbon, Portugal: MPAT, SEARN

Dillingh, D. (1992) *Zeespiegelstijging, getijverandering en Deltaveiligheid.* Report DGW-92. (Draft). October. Netherlands: DGW

ECON (1993) *The River Restoration Project, Phase 1: the feasibility study.* Report to the River Restoration Project. Norwich, UK: University of East Anglia

El-Jabi, N. and Ronselle, J. (1987) A Flood Damage Model for Flood Plain Studies. *Water Research Bulletin,* 23 (2), 179–87

Emery, J. (1986) *Disaster, Distress, Disease.* London, UK: Middlesex University, Flood Hazard Research Centre

Erikson, T. (1976) Loss of Community at Buffalo Creek. *American Journal of Psychiatry,* 133 (3), 302–5

EUROflood Project (1992) *Inception Report.* London, UK: Middlesex University, Flood Hazard Research Centre

EUROflood Project (1993) *First Annual Report.* London, UK: Middlesex University, Flood Hazard Research Centre

Folkmam, S. and Lazarus, R.S. (1980) An Analysis of Coping in a Middle-aged Community Sample. *Journal of Health and Social Behaviour,* 21, 219–39

Fordham, M.H. (1992) Choice and Constraints in Flood Hazard Mitigation: the environmental attitudes of floodplain residents and engineers. Unpublished PhD thesis. London, UK: Middlesex University

Fordham, M.H. (1993) Valuing the environment: the attitudes of flood plain residents and flood defence engineers. *Proceedings of the Values and the Environment Conferences,* 163–9. University of Surrey

Foster, H.D. (1980) *Disaster Planning: the preservation of life and property.* Berlin, Germany: Springer Verlag

Gardiner, J.L. (1988) Environmentally Sensitive River Engineering: examples from the Thames catchment. In Petts, G. (ed.). *Regulated Rivers: research and management,* vol. 2. Chichester, UK: John Wiley and Sons

Gardiner, J.L. (1991) Influences on the Development of River Catchment Planning in the Thames Basin. Unpublished PhD thesis. Southampton, UK: University of Southampton

Gleser, G.C.; Green, B.L. and Winger, C.W. (1981) *Prolonged Psychological Effects of Disaster: a study of Buffalo Creek.* New York, USA: Academic Press

Government of the Netherlands (1989a) *Algemene regels ter verzekering van de beveiliging door waterkeringen tegen overstromingen door het buitenwater en regeling van enkele daarmee verband houdende aangelegenheden* (Wet op de Waterkering) (Dutch Flood Protection Act). Tweede Kamer de Staten-Generaal. Vergaderjaar 1988–9, 21, 195, nos 1–2. SDU Uitgeverij. The Hague, Netherlands

Green, C.H. (1988) *The Relationship between Flooding, Stress and Health.* Paper given to the London meeting of the British Psychological Society

Green, C.H. (1991) Enabling Effective Hazard Management by the Public. In Parker, D. and Handmer, J. (eds) *Hazard Management and Emergency Planning: perspectives on Britain,* 175–93. London, UK: James and James

Green, C.H. (1993) *The Transferability of Flood Loss Estimation Data between*

Countries. Report to SIEE. London, UK: Middlesex University, Flood Hazard Research Centre

Green, C.H.; Emery, P.J.; Penning-Rowsell, E.C. and Parker, D.J. (1985) *The Health Effects of Flooding: a survey at Uphill, Avon.* London, UK: Middlesex University, Flood Hazard Research Centre

Green, C.H. and Newsome, D. (1992) *Ethics and the Calculi of Choice.* Paper given at the Stockholm Water Symposium, 10–14 August 1992. London, UK: Middlesex University, Flood Hazard Research Centre

Green, C.H.; N'Jai, A. and Neal, J. (1987) *Thames Overview Pre-feasibility Study. Report to Thames Water Authority.* London, UK: Middlesex University, Flood Hazard Research Centre

Green, C.H. and Penning-Rowsell, E.C. (1986) Evaluating the Intangible Benefits and Costs of a Flood Alleviation Proposal. *Journal of the Institution of Water Engineers and Scientists,* 40 (3), 229–48

Green, C.H. and Penning-Rowsell, E.C. (1989) Flooding and the Quantification of 'Intangibles'. *Journal of the Institution of Water and Environmental Management,* 3 (1), 27–30

Green, C.H. and Tunstall, S.M. (1991) The Evaluation of Water Quality Improvements by the Contingent Valuation Method. *Applied Economics,* 23, 1135–46

Green, C.H. and Tunstall, S.M. (1993) *The Ecological and Recreational Value of River Corridors: an economic perspective.* Paper given at the Ecological Basis for River Management Symposium, Leicester, UK

Green, C.H.; Tunstall, S.M. and Fordham, M. (1991) The Risks from Flooding: which risks and whose perceptions? *Disasters,* 15 (3), 227–36

Greenaway, M.A. and Smith, D.I. (1983) *ANUFLOOD Field Guide.* Canberra, Australia: Centre for Resource and Environmental Studies, Australian National University

Grigg, N.S. and Helweg, O.J. (1975) State-of-the-art of Estimating Flood Damage in Urban Areas. *Water Resources Bulletin,* 11 (2), 379–90

Günther, W. (1987) *Schadensanalyse des Innhochwassers in August 1985 für den Bereich der Gemeinde Krailburg.* Munich, Germany: Bayerisches Landesamt für Wasserwirtschaft

Günther, W. and Niekamp, O. (1989) *HOWAS – Hockwasserschadensdaten-Datenverwaltung und Auswertung* (HOWAS – Flood Damage Data – Data Handling and Processing). Beitragssammlung zum 2. Aachen, Germany: Fortbildungslehrgang Wasserwirtschaft des DVWK

Günther, W. and Schmidtke, R.F. (1988) Hochwasserschadensanalysen – Pilotuntersuchung über das Inn-Hochwasser im August 1985 (Flood Damage Analyses – Pilot Investigation on the River Inn Flood in August 1985). *Wasserwirtschaft,* 78 (2), 61–8

Handmer, J.W. (1994) *EUROflood Country Reports for France and Portugal.* Internal report to Middlesex University Flood Hazard Research Centre

Handmer, J.W. and Penning-Rowsell, E.C. (eds) (1990) *Hazards and the Communication of Risk.* Aldershot, UK: Gower Technical Press

Hargest, K.W.; Freeman, A.S.; Scanlon, D.A.; Turner, R.K. and Bateman, I.N. (1991) *Environmental Appraisal: a review of monetary evaluation and other techniques.* Report to the Transport and Road Research Centre. Birmingham, UK: Rendel Planning

Health and Safety Executive (1988) *The Tolerability of Risk from Nuclear Power Stations.* London, UK: HMSO

Higgins, R.J. (1981) *An Economic Comparison of Different Flood Mitigation Strategies in Australia.* Unpublished PhD thesis. School of Civil Engineering, University of New South Wales

Higgins, R.J. and Robinson, D.K. (1980) *The Assessment of Urban Flood Damages.* Paper given at the Symposium on Hydrology and Water Resources, Adelaide, Australia

Homan, A.G. and Waybur, B. (1960) *A Study of Procedure in Estimating Flood Damage to Residential, Commercial and Industrial Properties in California.* Merlo Park, CA, USA: Stanford Research Institute

Hoozemans, F.M.J. (1989) Analyse van windgegevens van lichtschepen voor de Nederlandse kust. Nota GWAO 89.010. Netherlands: Rijkswaterstaat, Dienst Getijdewateren

Huerta, F. and Horton, R. (1978) Coping Behaviour of Elderly Flood Victims. *Gerontologist,* 18, 541–6

Huybrechts, P. and Oerlemans, J. (1990) Response of the Antarctic ice sheet to future greenhouse warming. *Climate Dynamics,* 5, 93–102

IPCC (1990) *Climate Change. Scientific Assessment.* Report prepared for the IPCC by Working Group 1 (Houghton, J.T.; Jenkins, G.J. and Ephraums, J.J., eds)

IPCC (1992) *Climate Change 1992.* Supplementary Report to the IPCC Scientific Assessment. Report prepared for IPCC by Working Group 1 (Houghton, J.T.; Callander, B.A. and Varney, S.K.)

IPCC (1992) *Global Climate Change and the Rising Challenge of the Sea.* Response Strategies Working Group. Coastal Zone Management Subgroup

IPCC (1992) *Preliminary Guidelines for Assessing Impacts of Climate Change.* Working group 2 of the IPCC

IUCC (1993) *Climate Change Dossier.* Chatelaine, Switzerland: United Nations Environment Programme (UNEP)

Izard, J. (1972) *Ecological-economic Analysis for Regional Development.* New York, USA: The Free Press

Jelgersma, S. (1992) Vulnerability of the Coastal Lowlands of the Netherlands to a Future Sea-level Rise. In Tooley, M.J. and Jelgersma, S. (eds) (1992) *Impacts of Sea-level Rise on European Coastal Lowlands.* The Institute of British Geographers, Oxford, UK: Blackwell Publishers

Kates, R.W. (1962) *Hazard and Choice Perception in Flood Plain Management.* Department of Geography Research Paper 78. Chicago, USA: University of Chicago

Kates, R.W. (1978) *Risk Assessment of Environmental Hazard.* Chichester, UK: John Wiley and Sons

Keeney, R.L. and Raiffa, H. (1976) *Decisions with Multiple Objectives: preferences and value trade-offs.* New York, USA: John Wiley

Keeney, R.L. and Winterfeldt, D.V. (1986) Improving Risk Communication. *Risk Analysis,* 6 (4), 417–24

Klaus, J. (ed.) (1984) *Entscheidungshilfen für die Infrastrukturplanung* (Decision Support System for Assessing Technical Infrastructure). Baden-Baden, Germany: Nomos Verlag

Klaus, J.; Lindstadt, H.-J. and Pflügner, W. (1981) *Bewertung wasserwirtschaftlicher Infrastruktur* (Assessment of Water Resources Infrastructure). Germany: Münster-Hiltrup

Klaus, J. and Schmidtke, R.F. (1990) *Bewertungsgutachten für Deichbauvorhaben an der Festlandsküste* (Investment Appraisal for Coastal Flood Defence Schemes). Bonn, Germany: Der Bundesminister für Ernährung, Landwirtschaft und Forsten

Krutilla, J.V. and Fisher, A.C. (1975) *The Economics of Natural Environments.* Baltimore, USA: Johns Hopkins Press

Krzysztofowicz, R. and Davis, R. (1983) A Methodology for Evaluation of Flood Forecast-response Systems. *Water Resources Research,* 19 (6), 1423–54

Kwadijk, J.C.J. (1991) Sensitivity of the River Rhine Discharge to Environmental Change: a first tentative assessment. *Earth Surface Processes and Landforms,* 16, 627–37

Kwadijk, J.C.J. and Middelkoop, H. (1992) Estimation of the Impact of Climate Change on the Peak Discharge Probability of the River Rhine. Submitted to *Climate Change*

Labrijn, A. (1945) Het klimaat van Nederland gedurende de laatste twee en een halve eeuw. *Mededelingen en Verhandelingen van het KNMI,* 49

Langendoen, E.J. (1987) *Onderzoek naar de vergroting van het getijverschil te Vlissingen.* Report no. 5-87. Delft, Netherlands: Technical University

Laska, S.B. (1990) Homeowner Adaption to Flooding: an application of the general hazards coping theory. *Environment and Behaviour,* 22 (3), 320–57

Lave, T.R. and Lave, L.B. (1991) Public Perception of the Risks of Floods: implications for communication. *Risk Analysis,* 2 (2), 255–67

Lazarus, R.S. (1966) *Psychological Stress and the Coping Process.* New York, USA: Academic Press/McGraw-Hill

Lima, L. (1989) *Contributes para o Estudo da representação do Risco.* Lisbon, Portugal: LNEC

Lima, M.L. (1993) *Percepção de Riscos Ambientais: Representações e Identidades Sociais.* Communicação no I Colóquio de 'Ambiente': 4, Educação e Política Ambientais. Lisbon, Portugal: ISPA

Lind, R.C. (1982) A Primer on the Major Issues Relating to the Discount Rate for Evaluating National Energy Options. In Lind, R.C. (ed.) *Discounting for Time and Risk in Energy Policy.* Washington DC, USA: Resources for the Future

LNEC (1986) *Estudo Hidrológico e Hidráulico das Cheias e Inundações na Cidade de Setúbal* (Hydrologic and Hydraulic Study of Floods in the Town of Setúbal). Relatórios 245 e 246/86. Lisbon, Portugal: NHHF

Loucks, D.P. (1992) Water Resources Systems Models: their role in planning. *Journal of Water Resources Planning and Management,* 118 (3), 214–23

Louisse, C.J. and Kuik, A.J. (1990) Coastal Defence Alternatives in The Netherlands. In *The Dutch Coast* (Report of a session of the 22nd International Conference on Coastal Engineering 1990). Ministry of Transport and Public Works/Rijkswaterstaat. Delft, Netherlands: Delft Hydraulics

Louviere, J.J. (1988) *Analyzing Decision Making: motive conjoint analysis.* Newbury Park, CA, USA: Sage Publications

McLuckie, B.J. (1973) *The Warning System in Disaster Situations: a selective analysis.*

Disaster Research Center Research Series, no. 9. Ohio, USA: Ohio State University
Merkblatter zur Wasserwirtschaft (1989) *Wahl des bemessungshochwassers.*
Hamburg, Germany: Paul Parey
Miller, J.A.; Turner, J.G. and Kimball, E. (1981) Big Thompson Flood Victims:
one year later. *Family Relations,* 30, 111–16
Ministry of Agriculture, Fisheries and Food (1993) *Flood and Coastal Defence Project
Appraisal Guidance Note.* London, UK: Ministry of Agriculture, Fisheries and Food
Ministry of Housing, Physical Planning and the Environment (1991) Onze ken-
nis over klimaatverandering, verslag van een workshop. Report no. Lucht 99.
Netherlands: Ministry of Housing, Physical Planning and the Environment
Ministry of Housing, Physical Planning and the Environment (1992) *The
Netherlands' Memorandum on Climate Change: Executive Summary.* CCD/Paper 4,
April 1992. Netherlands: Ministry of Housing, Physical Planning and the
Environment
Ministry of Public Health, Physical Planning and Environment (1992) *CHANGE*
(Research and policy newsletter on global change from the Netherlands), 11
October. Netherlands: Ministry of Public Health, Physical Planning and
Environment
Ministry of Transport and Public Works (1990) *A New Coastal Defence Policy for the
Netherlands.* The Hague, Netherlands: Ministry of Transport and Public Works
Mitchell, R.C. and Carson, R.T. (1989) *Usuing Surveys to Value Public Goods: the
contingent valuation method.* Washington DC, USA: Resources for the Future
Moore, H.E. (1964) *And the Winds Blew.* Austin, Texas, USA: University of Texas
Naess, A. (1993) The Deep Ecological Movement: Some philosophical aspects.
In Armstrong, S. and Botzler, R.G. (eds) *Environmental Ethics – Divergence and
Convergence.* New York, USA: McGraw-Hill
National Institute of Mental Health (1979) *Crisis Intervention Programs for Disaster
Victims in Smaller Communities.* Washington DC, USA: US Department of Health
and Human Services
Newsome, D.W. and Green, C.H. (1993) *Economic Value of Changes to the Water
Environment.* RID Note 37, Bristol, UK: National Rivers Authority
Nijkamp, P.; Rietveld, P. and Voogd, H. (1990) *Multicriteria Evaluation in Physical
Planning.* Amsterdam, North Holland
Nijkamp, P. and Van Delft, A. (1977) Multicriteria Analysis and Regional
Decisionmaking. *Studies in Applied Regional Science,* 8. Nijhoff, Leiden,
Netherlands
Nordhaus, W.D. (1993) *Managing the Global Commons: the economics of climate change.*
Cambridge, Mass, USA: Massachusetts Institute of Technology (MIT) Press
OECD (1993) *Coastal Zone Management: integrated policies.* Paris, France: OECD
OECD (1993) *Coastal Zone Management: selected case studies.* Paris, France: OECD
Oerlemans, J. (1993) Factors Contributing to Sea Level Rise on a Decade to
Century Time Scale. For: Sea Level Change and their Consequences for
Hydrology and Water Management. Noordwijkerhout, Netherlands, 19–23 April
Oerlemans, J. and Fortuin, J.P.F. (1992) Sensitivity of Glaciers and Small Ice
Caps to Greenhouse Warming. *Science,* 258, 2 October
Parker, D.J. (1991) *The Damage-reducing Effects of Flood Warnings.* London, UK:

Middlesex University, Flood Hazard Research Centre

Parker, D.J.; Green, C.H. and Thompson, P.M. (1987) *Urban Flood Protection Benefits: a project appraisal guide (The Red Manual).* Aldershot, UK: Gower Technical Press

Parker, D.J. and Handmer, J. (1992) *Hazard Management and Emergency Planning: perspectives on Britain.* London, UK: James and James

Parker, D.J. and Neal, J. (1990) Evaluating the Performance of Flood Warning Systems. In Handmer, J.W. and Penning-Rowsell, E.C. (eds) *Hazard and the Communication of Risk,* 137–56. Aldershot, UK: Gower Technical Press

Parker, D.J.; Penning-Rowsell, E.C. and Green, C.H. (1983) *Swalecliffe Coast Protection Proposals: evaluation of potential benefits.* London, UK: Middlesex University, Flood Hazard Research Centre

Parker, D.J. and Tunstall, S.M. (1991) Managing Flood Warning Systems: the United Kingdom experience. Annual Conference of the Association of Floodplain Managers. Denver, Colorado, 11 June

Pearce, D.W. and Turner, R.K. (1990) *Economics of Natural Resources and the Environment.* New York, USA: Harvester Wheatsheaf

Pearce, D.W. and Warford, J.J. (1993) *World Without End.* New York, USA: Oxford University Press

Peerbolte, E.B. (1993) *Sea-level Rise and Safety.* Twente, Netherlands: University of Twente

Peerbolte, E.B.; Baarse, G.; de Ronde, J.G. and de Vrees, L. (1991) *Impact of Sea Level Rise on Society, a case study for the Netherlands.* Final Report, H750. Netherlands: Rijkswaterstaat and Delft Hydraulics

Penning-Rowsell, E.C. (1976) The Effect of Flood Damage on Land Use Planning. *Geographica Polonica,* 34, 139–53

Penning-Rowsell, E.C. (1986) The Development of Integrated Flood Warning Systems. In Smith, D.I. and Handmer, J.W. (eds) *Flood Warning in Australia,* 15–36. Canberra, Australia: Centre for Resource and Environmental Studies, Australian National University

Penning-Rowsell, E.C. and Chatterton, J.B. (1977) *The Benefits of Flood Alleviation: a manual of assessment techniques (The Blue Manual).* Aldershot, UK: Gower Technical Press

Penning-Rowsell, E.C.; Chatterton, J.B.; Day, H.J.; Ford, D.T.; Greenaway, M.A.; Smith, D.I.; Wood, T.R. and Witts, R.W. (1987) Comparative Aspects of Computerized Floodplain Data Management. *Journal of Water Resources Planning and Management,* 113 (6), 725–44

Penning-Rowsell, E.C.; Green, C.H.; Thompson, P.M.; Coker, A.M.; Tunstall, S.M.; Richards, C. and Parker, D.J. (1992) *The Economics of Coastal Management: a manual of assessment techniques.* London, UK: Belhaven Press

Penning-Rowsell, E.C. and Handmer, J. (1988) Flood Hazard Management in Britain: a changing scene. *Geographical Journal,* 154 (2), 209–20

Penning-Rowsell, E.C.; Parker, D.J.; Crease, D. and Mattison, C.R. (1983) *Flood Warning Dissemination: an evaluation of some current practices in the Severn-Trent Water Authority area.* Geography and Planning Papers, no. 7. London, UK: Middlesex University, Flood Hazard Research Centre

Penning-Rowsell, E.C.; Parker, D.J. and Harding, D.M. (1986) *Floods and Drainage: British policies for hazard reduction, agricultural improvement and wetland conservation.* London, UK: Allen and Unwin

Penning-Rowsell, E.C.; Peerbolte, B.; Correia, F.N.; Fordham, M.; Green, C.H.; Pflügner, W.; Rocha, J.; Saraiva, M.; Schmidtke, R.; Torterotot, J. and Van der Veen, A. (1992) Flood Vulnerability Analysis and Climate Change: towards a European methodology. In Saul, A.J. (ed.) *Floods and Flood Management.* Dordrecht, Germany: Kluwer Academic Publishers

Pflügner, W. (1988) *Nutzenanalysen im Umweltschutz – Der ökonomische Wert von Wasser und Luft* (Benefit Analysis in Environmental Protection – The Economic Value of Water and Air). Göttingen, Germany: Vanden Hoeck and Ruprecht

Plazak, D.J. (1986) Flood Control Benefits Revisited. *Journal of Water Resources Planning and Management,* 112 (2), 265–76

Poulshock, S.W. and Cohen, E.S. (1975) The Elderly in the Aftermath of a Disaster. *Gerontology,* 5, 357–61

Powell, B. and Penick, E. (1983) Psychological Distress Following a Natural Disaster: a one year follow-up of 98 flood victims. *Journal of Community Psychology,* 2, 269–76

Price, J. (1978) Some Age-related Effects of the 1974 Brisbane Floods. *Australian and New Zealand Journal of Psychiatry,* 12, 55–8

Quarantelli, F. (1985) What is a Disaster: the need for clarification in definition and conceptualization in research. In Sowder, B. (ed.) *Disasters and Mental Health.* Washington DC, USA: National Institute of Mental Health

Ramos, I. (1992) *As Quintas Envolventes de Setúbal.* Uma Proposta de Ordenamento. Final Report for the Degree of Landscape Architecture. Lisbon, Portugal: ISA

Rijkswaterstaat (1989) *Kustverdediging na 1990. Discussienota.* The Hague, Netherlands: Ministry of Transport and Public Works

River Planning Division (1990) *Investigation of River Economy.* Tokyo, Japan: River Bureau, Ministry of Construction

Rocha, J. (1988) *Erosao NA Serra Do Algrave Relatorio Final.* Relatorio LENEC 112/89

Rochford, E.B. and Blocker, T.J. (1991) Coping with 'Natural' Hazards as Stressor: the predictor of activism in a flood disaster. *Environment and Behaviour,* 23 (2)

Ronde, J.G. de and Heinen, P.F. (1993) *Tide Gauge Records along the Dutch Coast.* The Hague, Netherlands: Ministry of Transport, Public Works and Water Management

Ronde, J.G. de and Vogel, J.A. (1988) *Technical Report 6* (TR6). Zeespiegelrijzing. Hydro Meteo scenario's. Note GWA0-88.015. February

Saraiva, M. da G. (1987) *A Defesa contra Cheias e sua Inserçâo no Ordenamento do Território.* Area Metropolitana de Lisboa (Flood Defence and Land Use Planning. Lisbon Metropolitan area). MSc thesis in Urban and Regional Planning. Lisbon, Portugal: UTL

Saraiva, M. da G.; Pinto, P., Rabaca, J.; Ramos, A. and Revez, M. (1992) *Protection, Reduction and Improvement of Small Watercourses in the Suburbs of Evora, Portugal.* Paper given at international symposium 'The Ecological Basis for River Management', Leicester, UK

Saul, A.J. (ed.) (1992) *Floods and Flood Management.* Dordrecht, Netherlands: Kluwer Academic Publishers

Schmidtke, R.F. (1993) Estimation of Flood Damage Potentials as Planning Information for Coast Protection Sea Defence Schemes. *Proceedings of the International UNESCO Workshop 'Sea Level Changes and their Consequences for Hydrology and Water Management'.* Nordwijkerhout, Netherlands. Session IC: Socio-economic Impacts, 75–88. Koblenz, Germany: IHP/OHP National Committee of Germany

Sewell, W.R.D. (1971) Environmental Perceptions and Attitudes of Engineers and Public Health Officials. *Environment and Behaviour,* March, 23–59

Sewell, W.R.D. (1974) The Role of Perceptions of Professionals in Environmental Decision Making. In Coppock, J.T. and Wilson, C.B. (eds), *Environmental Quality,* 109–31. Edinburgh, UK: Scottish Academic Press

Sewell, W.R.D. and Little, B.R. (1973) Specialists, Laymen and the Process of Environmental Appraisal. *Regional Studies,* 7, 161–71

SIEE (1993) Analyse Empirique de l'Apparition des Désordres et des Dommages résultant des différentes crues dans l'agglomeration continue d'Ile-de-France. Report to Institution Interdépartementale des Barrages Réservoirs du Bassin de la Seine. Montpellier, France: Société d'Ingénierie pour l'Eau et l'Environnement

Siegmund, P.C. (1990) *The Effect of Doubling of Atmospheric CO_2 on the Stormtracks in the Climate of a General Circulation Model.* Scientific report WR90-01. Royal Netherlands Meteorological Institute

Slovic, P. (1986) Informing and Educating the Public about Risk. *Risk Analysis,* 6 (4), 403–15

Smith, D.I. and Handmer, J.W. (eds) (1986) *Flood Warning in Australia.* Canberra, Australia: Centre for Resource and Environmental Studies, Australian National University

Suleman, M.; N'Jai, A.; Green, C.H. and Penning-Rowsell, E.C. (1988) *Potential Flood Damage: a major update.* London, UK: Middlesex University, Flood Hazard Research Centre

Tapsell, S.M.; Fordham, M.; Tunstall, S.M. and Horne, M. (1991) *The River Environment and You – Postal Survey: Datchet to Walton Bridge.* Draft Final Report. London, UK: Middlesex University, Flood Hazard Research Centre

Torterotot, J.P. (1988) *Organisation et réalisation d'enquêtes sur les dommages dus aux innodations.* Noisy-le-Grand, France: CERGRENE

Torterotot, J.P. (1993) Analysis of Individual Responses to Flood Warning and Influence on Damage in Various Regions of France. In EUROflood Project, *First Annual Report,* 179–318. London, UK: Middlesex University

Torterotot, J.P. (1993) *Le coût des dommages dus aux inondations: estimation et analyse des incertitudes* (The cost of damage due to flooding: assessment and uncertainty analysis). Doctoral thesis. Paris, France: Ecole Nationale des Ponts et Chaussées

Torterotot, J.P.; Kauark-Leite, L.A. and Roche, P.A. (1992) Analysis of Individual Real-time Responses to Flooding and Influence on Damage to Households. In Saul, A.J. (ed.) *Floods and Flood Management,* 363–87. Dordrecht, Netherlands: Klumer Academic Publishers

Torterotot, J.P. and Roche, P.A. (1990) Evaluations socio-économiques pour la gestion du risque d'inondation. Paper given at the European Conference of Water Management, Paris, 4–6 December. In *La gestion de l'eau*, 481–90. Paris, France: Presses de l'Ecole Nationale des Ponts et Chaussées.

Tunstall, S.M. and Bossman-Aggrey, P. (1988) *Waltham Abbey and Thornwood, Essex: an assessment of the effects of the flood of 29th July 1987 and the benefits of flood alleviation*. London, UK: Middlesex University, Flood Hazard Research Centre

Tunstall, S. and Fordham, M. (1990) *Thames Perception and Attitude Survey – Datchet to Walton Bridge*. Draft Final Report. London, UK: Middlesex University, Flood Hazard Research Centre

US Water Resources Council (1983) *Economic and Environmental Principles and Guidelines for Water and Related Land Resources Implementation Studies*. Washington DC, USA: Department of the Interior

Van der Veen, A. and Wierstra, A. (1993) Full Flood Impacts Decision Support Methods. In EUROflood Project, *First Annual Report*, 45–67. London, UK: Middlesex University

Verdin and Morel-Seytoux (1981) *User's Manual for XSRAIN – a Fortran IV Programme for Calculation of Flood Hydrografics for Ungaged Watershed*. Federal Highway Administration. Washington DC, USA

Walthern, P. (ed.) (1988) *Environmental Impact Assessment*. London, UK: Unwin Hyman

Ward, R. (1978) *Floods: a geographical perspective*. London, UK: Macmillan

Wenger, D.E. (1978) Community Response to Disaster: functional and structural alterations. In Quarantelli, E.L. (ed.) *Disasters, Theory and Research*. Beverly Hills, California, USA: Sage Publications Inc.

Wenger, D.E. and Weller, J.M. (1978) *Disaster Subcultures: the cultural residues of community disasters*. Disaster Research Center Paper 9. Columbus, Ohio, USA

White, G.F. (1966) Formation and Role of Public Attitudes. In Jarett, H. (ed.) *Environmental Quality in a Growing Economy*. Baltimore, USA: Johns Hopkins Press

White, G.F. (1966) Optimal Flood Damage Management. In Kneese, A.V. and Smith, S.C. (eds) *Water Research*, 251–69. Baltimore, USA: Johns Hopkins Press for Resources for the Future

Wigley, T.M.L. and Raper, S.C.B. (1992) Implications for Climate and Sea Level of Revised IPCC Emissions Scenarios. *Nature*, 357, 28 May

Williams, H.B. (1964) Human Factors in Warning-and-response Systems. In Grosser, G.; Wechsler, H. and Greenblatt, M. (eds) *The Threat of Impending Disaster: contributions to the psychology of stress*. Cambridge, Mass, USA: Massachusetts Institute of Technology (MIT) Press

Winterfeldt, D. von and Edwards, W. (1986) *Decision Analysis and Behavioural Research*. Cambridge, UK: Cambridge University Press

World Coast Conference Organizing Committee (1993) *How to Account for Impacts. Concepts and Tools*. The Hague, Netherlands: World Coast Conference Organizing Committee

Index